FUNDAMENTALS OF TECHNOLOGY

Volume One

Second Edition

DeWayne R. Brown, PhD
Derrek B. Dunn, PhD

Change the course.

530 Great Road
Acton, Massachusetts 01720
800-562-2147

This book is dedicated to the most influential and inspirational women in Dewayne's life:

Mrs. Dora Mae Hanna Brown Redden (Mother)

Mrs. Josephine Coward Hanna (Grandmother) [deceased]

Dr. Lisa Hope Antoine

Ms. Arneitha Roberta Nesmith

Dr. Cynthia Thompson

CONTENTS

PREFACE

This book is intended to be used for students at vocational, associate or baccalaureate degree programs who are studying to become technicians or technologists. The book will start with a comprehensive review of the past and the present history of technology. The various careers in technology will be covered. The role of the technologist in the technical lab will be emphasized. The book will provide information about student success that will help them with retention and realizing their personal goal. Students will begin preparing for their careers in technology by developing cover letters, writing resumes, learning to critique interviews and will receive valuable advice for effective writing and listening. Topics that will be vital to students' careers, in the private sector and government such as leadership and diversity, will be included. The fundamental mathematics and measurements that are used in various fields in technology is studied. Plotting data and statistics will be covered where MATLAB will be used as the instrumental tool for computation and graphing.

Changes in the Second Edition

- The most extensive improvements in the *Fundamentals of Technology, Second Edition* are:

- Employ and salary information in Chapter 1 has been updated.

- History of Technology has been updated to reflect the second decade of the 21st century.

- The section on Ethics and Professionalism for Computer Professionals in Chapter 2 was updated to reflect new information on copyright laws, trademark, servicemark and patents.

- A new section was added to Chapter 2 to address six types of interviews.

- More information was added in Chapter 2 for preparing for the initial interview (screening interview) and the on-site interview (selection interview).

- A new section was added to Chapter 2 that provide information on the tone of voice during interview.

- A new section was created in Chapter 2 to help students address tough job interview questions.

- There is a new chapter on effective communication skills.

- There is new chapter on leadership and diversity.

- There is a new chapter featuring student success.

To the Student

Today, the key to survival in the fierce job market will involve the embracement of diversity and the employment of people with capable leadership potential. Corporations and their customers have been forced to react not only to the changing face of America, but the mindsets of the global marketplace. Innovation will continue to thrive even in the online world. The demand for professionals to produce, install, and maintain state-of-the-art equipment, train and supervise industry's skilled workers, and support research and development efforts will remain on the rise. This book will allow you to answer questions like:

- How can I start now and continue to persist to my goals of graduation and job employment?

- Am I communicating effectively and managing my time efficiently?

- What challenges am I facing to remain productive in my technical career as corporations reinvent themselves with diversity?

This textbook will provide a lot of information for succeeding in college, preparing for a career after graduation and maintaining your success through your professional years. Emphasis is placed on ethics, attitude, professionalism, communicating effectively, valuableness of find resources and using your time wisely. The authors encourage the students to sharpen their problem-solving abilities by working the math problems because it will help them build their critical thinking skills.

To the Instructor

The text material has been used in the classroom and has worked well for our four-year college students who pursued a bachelor's degree in technology. It usage is encouraged for two-year college students, too. This book is user-friendly for students without a strong background in technology. *Fundamentals of Technology, Second Edition* is recommended to be used as the primary text for Orientation to Technology or Engineering Technology courses or as a supplement for courses requiring the use of applied mathematics, computers, or scientific calculators. The text also may be used in technical or vocational schools.

All chapters of the textbook have a homework section in Appendix A. Chapters 1 – 6 consist of comprehension that will help reinforce the concepts from the chapters. Some of the comprehension will require consulting resources outside the book, such as the internet to stimulate critical thinking. Chapters 7 – 10 contain numerous practical applications, computer simulation/scientific calculator computations, and critical-thinking mathematical problems to help the students to think more abstractly and be able to analyze.

Organization

Chapter 1 will provide an introduction to technology. First the history of technology will be discussed, from the Stone Age through the second decade of the 21th Century. Various growing fields in technology such as Information Technology (IT), Computer Engineering (CET), Biomedical Technology, and Environmental Technology are investigated. The differences among the job responsibilities of scientists, engineers, technologists and technicians are examined.

Chapter 2 focuses on the career development of a technologist. The importance of professionalism and ethics are covered. Emphasis is placed on personal and professional development, work habits and job performance, personal conduct and human relations. Tips and pointers on cover letters, and resumes for hard copy and email are featured. There are samples of cover letters and resumes. Students are taught how to write letters to acknowledge an offer as well as how to reject an offer. The textbook will cover the entire process of preparing for interviews whether if it is an initial or on-site interview and whether it is in person, by telephone, by computer or will be video-conferenced. Addition information on the tone of voice during interviews is provided. There is a valuable section that addresses how to respond to sample tough interview questions.

In **Chapter 3** the job responsibilities of the technologist in the technical laboratory will be discussed. The importance of lab safety training is covered. Some rules for lab safety are offered. How to develop good lab skills is addressed. The types of errors that occur in measurements in the laboratory such as gross, systematic, and random are reviewed. Strategies for reducing these errors are included. Percentage error calculations are done. The importance of significant figures and their effects on computations are emphasized. In addition, how to write lab reports and tips on giving oral reports are discussed in this chapter, too. A brief review of common errors in lab reports is given. Some popular technological tools to enhance performance in the technical laboratory as well as the classroom, such as the scientific graphical calculator and the computer algebraic systems are covered.

Chapter 4 addresses how to communicate effectively. The chapter emphasizes the process of how communication works. Students will learn how to communicate exactly what they want to say and what mode of communication is best for that particular message. In addition, factors that influence your ability to speak clearly and listen critically are discussed. This chapter addresses the four types of communication styles and provides advice on how to communicate if you have that style or dealing with someone else who has that style.

In **Chapter 5** the importance of leadership and diversity are emphasized. Leadership is defined and its attributes and qualities are described. This chapter will help students to develop leadership skills to be successful leaders through education and modeling leadership rubrics. The importance of embracing diversity as a culture is addressed. Factors that affect diversity will be covered to help students appreciate and market the

new direction that corporations are now taking to implement diversity and inclusion in their infrastructures. Students will learn first-hand hoe companies and institutions are re-inventing themselves through diversity matrices and competency models for diversity management from domestic and global perspectives. Students will understand the newly role of Diversity & Inclusion (D&I) practitioners in the corporate and the visionary and strategic planning that they must bring to help corporations remain successful.
.

Chapter 6 explains how student success is beneficial to society. The most potent principles of student success are identified in this chapter. The factors that influence students' success in college are addressed. This chapter is helpful for freshmen students who are making that transition to college by providing advice and recommendations for common changes and common stressors that freshmen can expect in their first year on campus. Student time management is emphasized and some of the common barriers to student time management are discussed. Advice will be offered for improvement of techniques for studying.

Chapter 7 will cover some of the basic mathematics used in the various fields of technology. Topics such as arithmetic, simple algebraic equations, and basic matrix algebra are covered. MATLAB as a software simulation tool for computation will be introduced in this chapter as reinforcement of the learned concepts. Computer software tools such as MATLAB will be valuable for students entering the corporate work environment or graduate school. MATLAB is one of the most powerful and popular software tools for science-related fields on the market. MATLAB is a programming language and data visualization tool. MATLAB has many capabilities for solving problems in engineering, technology, scientific, computing and mathematical disciplines.

Chapter 8 covers measurement systems. First the U.S. customary system of measurement is discussed. Next the metric system is studied. Conversions between the U.S. customary and metric systems are performed. Temperature conversions are done. Mathematical applications that can be solved by the usage of a circle are addressed. The relationship among various units of time is covered. Lastly, students are taught how to effectively determine the time in different time zones.

Chapter 9 emphasizes the fundamentals of graphing data. After data is collected it must be presented to others in a meaningful way. Oscilloscopes, spectrum analyzers, logic analyzers etc. are examples of some of the instruments that display graphical information. Students will learn how to graph linear equations and non-linear equations. Selecting scales for graphs will be reviewed. The concepts of interpolation and extrapolation applications to graphing will be covered. In addition, students will use MATLAB to plot fundamental two-dimensional graphics. They will be able to graph trigonometric functions, such as the sine wave, cosine wave, and the tangent wave. They will be able to graph linear and non-linear equations. Students will be able to label the x- and y-axes. They will be able to give graphs a title name.

Chapter 10 covers the background of statistics. This chapter covers a range of techniques and procedures for analyzing data, interpreting data, and displaying data. In this chapter, students will use MATLAB to perform statistical analyses on data sets. They will compute the mean, standard deviation and variance of data sets by both hand calculation and computer simulation. Students will use MATHLAB to create histograms. They will apply MATLAB curve fitting techniques to data sets for straight-line approximation, quadratic approximation and other higher order approximations.

About the Authors

Dr. Dewayne Randolph Brown is a Full Professor of Computer Systems Technology Department within the School of Technology at North Carolina Agricultural & Technical State University in Greensboro, North Carolina, United States of America. Dr. Brown teaches undergraduate and graduates courses in electronic and wireless communications. In addition, Dr. Brown has taught orientation to technology courses for nine-teen years. Dr. Brown has written four previous textbooks relevant to the field of technology, *Fundamentals of Technology* (XanEdu, 2012), *Fundamental Mathematics for Electronics and Information Technology* (XanEdu, 2008), *Mathematics for Technologists in Electronics, Second Edition* (Prentice-Hall, 2002), and *Mathematics for Technologists in Electronics* (Pearson Custom Publishing, 2000). Dr. Brown received his Bachelors of Science in electrical engineering from the University of South Carolina in 1990. Dr. Brown received his Masters of Science in electrical engineering from North Carolina Agricultural & Technical State University in 1992. Dr. Brown received his Ph.D. in electrical engineering from Virginia Polytechnic Institute and State University in 1997. Dr. Brown has been a member of Association for Technology, Management, and Applied Engineers (ATMAE) formerly known as the National Association of Industrial Technology (NAIT) since 2000. Dr. Brown is a Certified Senior Technology Manager (CSTM) within ATMAE.

Dr. Derrek B. Dunn is currently a Full Professor and Chairperson of the Department of Technology in the School of Business and Technology at University of Maryland at Eastern Shore (UMES). Dr. Dunn has taught college level courses in such fields as Wireless Communication Systems, Computer Networks, Telecommunication Management, Global Positioning Systems, and Optical Systems.

Dr. Dunn received his Bachelor of Science in Electrical Engineering and a Bachelor of Science in Mathematics from North Carolina A&T State University. He also received a Master of Science in Electrical Engineering, Master of Science in Mathematics and a Doctor of Philosophy in Electrical Engineering from Virginia Polytechnic Institute and State University.

Dr. Dunn bring nearly 15 years of experience in teaching and research on learners and learning at a distance, and experience on the use of distance education in technology and engineering.

Dr. Dunn's past experience with The Association of Technology, Management, and Applied Engineering (ATMAE) formerly known as the National Association of Industrial Technology (NAIT) includes membership of NAIT/ATMAE for the past eleven years, certified industrial technologist, ATMAE accreditation training, Regional Director - Student Division and member and elected to a second term as Vice-President of the Electrical, Electronics and Computer Technology (EECT) Division and is currently the President of the Electrical, Electronics and Computer Technology (EECT) Division.

CHAPTER 1
Introduction to Technology

CHAPTER 1
INTRODUCTION TO TECHNOLOGY

1.1 HISTORY OF TECHNOLOGY

1.1.1 TECHNOLOGY THROUGH THE AGES

Since the very beginning of mankind, we have utilized tools and developed technology like spears to kill prey and knives to slaughter meat. During the passage of time, different technologies have come up to define different ages of man and civilization. Below is the history of technology based on different ages.

Figure 1.1

1.1.2 STONE AGE

During the Stone Age which roughly lasted about 2.5 million years ago as humans started to develop at about 3300 BC which began the Bronze Age during which several technologies developed. They needed little knowledge to harness these technologies yet they were helpful in keeping our species from getting extinct. Finally, the technologies and knowledge that were gained throughout the first 2.5 million years of existence helped humans to evolve from the Stone Age into the Bronze Age and during this time increasingly sophisticated tools and knowledge were adopted. Some of the technologies that were developed during the Stone Age included the use of stones and axes for killing prey, the ability to harness fire about 1.5 million years ago, clothing about 100,000 years ago, domesticating animals occurring about 15,000 years ago and other inventions such as the bow and arrow about 9,000 BC, Agriculture about 8,000 BC and the invention of wheel which occurred around 4,000 BC.

1.1.3 BRONZE AGE

The Bronze Age roughly lasted from 3300 BC to 1200 BC; it was that time when civilization started to come together around the Fertile Crescent and had spread outward to the continents of Europe, Asia and Africa. The 'Bronze Age' gets its name from a time when metals like copper and tin were being used to create weapons and tools. The technology to melt metal ores into tools was a definite advancement from the previous stone tools which was being used. Some of the further technologies that were highly developed during this age included the further domestication of animals, agricultural innovations, the chariot around 2,000 BC, the use of salt and the construction of permanent settlements, many of which still stand today.

1.1.4 THE IRON AGE

The Iron Age usually dates back from 1200 BC to 500 BC. This time was the start of Roman Empire and during this time, the usage of iron began to become prominent as a metal for tools and weapons and it is much stronger than tin, copper and bronze. It was also during this time period that many people migrated farther to the continents including Europe and permanent settlements were developed. In addition, during this time period several religions and philosophies were developed which included Confucianism and Buddhism. Other technological development included the sundial at about 800 BC, glass in 500 BC and a wide range of other advances in trade, education, ships, architecture, etc.

1.1.5 AGE OF ANCIENT CIVILATIONS

With the start of Roman Empire from around 500 BC to about 500 AD when it finally fell and the Medieval Europe took hold, there was a lot of technological innovation occurring. This period in human history is considered to be the Golden Age as civilizations hardened and technology in all aspects of human life expanded. It should also be noted that civilizations from around the globe began to grow such as in China, India, Europe, Africa, Middle East, Central and South America, etc. Some of the innovations that happened during this time included city planning, sanitation, education, architecture, bridges, matches, paper, religion, math, magnetic compass, law and government, canals, reservoirs, road building, stirrups for horses, concrete, art, philosophy and much more.

1.1.6 MIDDLE AGES

The middle Ages which lasted from 500 AD to about 1500 was an era in Europe where most part of technology either stood still or even went backwards. However, it should also be noted that with the Crusades and the increase of more trade and travel to the Middle East, Europe had once again began to grow and this growth in all areas of society guided the Renaissance period. While most part of Europe stagnated, there were several developments in technology including the mechanical clock, spectacles, windmill and innovations in agriculture, military and architecture.

1.1.7 MUSLIM AGRICULTURAL REVOLUTION

During the 8th century, Islamic world predominantly located in the Middle East revolutionized and eventually globalized a broad range of agriculture techniques and crops. In addition during this revolution, the hydropower was utilized in order to mill a variety of different crops along with innovations of other wide range uses. Other significant technological advances included the fountain pen, coffee, and quartz glass, innovations in math, shampoo, hard soap, nitric acid, incendiary devices and celestial globe.

1.1.8 RENAISSANCE PERIOD

As the trade between Middle East and Europe exploded during the time of crusades and as the Europeans thirst for knowledge grew, the Renaissance period started which is usually marked from 14th century to the 16th century. During this era, Europe prospered scientifically and artistically. Also during this time, some of the major innovations occurred in education. The printing press which was a major invention helped in spreading books throughout Europe and the world communicating a wide range of ideas and ultimately expanding education. Many schools and universities were also developed during this era. Philosophy, architecture and other subjects grew and expanded and not the least, medicine also enjoyed a rich host of innovation.

1.1.9 AGE OF EXPLORATION

As trade was becoming a great mean of wealth for countries in Europe, the Age of Exploration started to dominate the field of technology and innovation, mainly in shipping, navigation and cartography. Many ships sailed across the globe and around the world during this time which lasted from the 1400's to 1600's. The New World was discovered and settlements and colonization occurred along with the conquest of local and indigenous people.

1.1.9 INDUSTRIAL REVOLUTION

The Industrial Revolution was an era of great development due to adopting of cheap energy through coal and steam engine. These two innovations which had occurred mostly in Britain during the late 18th and 19th centuries was a landmark in human technology. With the ability of no longer relying on the water power, animal power or human power for farming and other uses, coal could be burned to drive steam engines for wide range of uses including factories, transportation including steam locomotives and steam ships, the ability of mass production of metals such as wrought iron and other metals to build bridges and other items. With the start of Industrial Revolution, the transportation revolution also came which made easier to transport people, livestock and goods all around Europe and the United States. Because of the Industrial Revolution, huge innovations began in economy and society as more and more people left agricultural communities and migrated to cities to live and work, this process helped pave the way for a society based on specialization.

Figure 1.2

1.1.10 THE 19TH AND 20TH CENTURIES

During the recent last two centuries, there were enormous innovations in technology. Although it is important to note that many of these innovations have occurred due to previous discoveries and cumulative amount of knowledge and technology that was developed over a course of time. Some of the huge innovations in technology that occurred during the last 200 years include massive changes in government, society, practically in every institution, electrification and science, inventions such as radio, television, telephone, computer, internet, automobile, airplane, medicine, economy, military weaponry, household appliances, refrigeration, sanitation, photography, nuclear power, spacecraft, mechanized agriculture and many more.

Today, we live in a society that has been vastly changed because of innovations and improvements from technology; this collective knowledge is growing at an increasing speed. While it took usually centuries in the past for society to be changed from technology but today, technology has a huge impact on our society in a matter of decades or even years. While it is not known what the future holds for technical innovations, with the thirst for knowledge and discovery is inborn in humans, we can be sure that more technological advances will be definitely seen on the horizon.

1.1.11 HISTORY OF INFORMATION TECHNOLOGY

1.1.11.1 THE 1950s

In 1957, the planar transistor was developed by Jean Hoerni. With this technology the integrated circuit became a reality. This process forces certain types of atoms to infuse into an otherwise pure piece of silicon. These impurities or dopants create the conducting and control structures of the transistors on the chip. With this technology, microscopic circuit boards could be laid out on the silicon surface, thus allowing the compacting of these circuits onto integrated circuits.

Also in 1957, a group of eight electronics engineers and physicists formed the Fairchild Semiconductor. In 1958, one of these men, Jack Kilby, produced the first integrated circuit for commercial use.

1.1.11.2 THE 1960s

In 1960, Advanced Research Projects Agency Network (ARPANET) was developed by the U. S. Department of Defense. It was originally intended as a network of government, university, research, and scientific computers. ARPANET was designed to enable researchers to share information. This government project eventually grew into the Internet as we know it today. The networking technology and topology was originally designed to survive nuclear attack. This was back during the Cold War era, when most scientists expected that the USA would be subject to a nuclear attack someday. The design required that the network would route traffic and data flow around any damage. This robustness enabled the Internet to grow at incredible speed, until today it serves up any of billions of web pages.

In 1962, the first recorded description of the social interactions that could be enabled through networking was a series of memos written by J.C.R. Licklider of Massachusetts Institute of Technology (MIT) in August 1962. He discussed his "Galactic Network" concept. He envisioned a globally interconnected set of computers through which everyone could quickly access data and programs from any site. In spirit, the concept was very much like the Internet of today. Licklider was the first head of the computer research program at Defense Advanced Research Projects Administration (DARPA), starting in October 1962. While at DARPA he convinced his successors at DARPA, Ivan Sutherland, Bob Taylor, and MIT researcher Lawrence G. Roberts, of the importance of this networking concept.

The Uniplexed Information and Computing System (UNIX) Operating System was developed in 1969. UNIX was developed at AT&T labs by engineers Ken Thompson and Dennis Ritchie. The UNIX operating system was the first operating system that ran on a minicomputer and could handle multitasking and networking. It was also written in the C programming language - then a high level language with power and flexibility. Other operating systems existed, but they were usually written in assembly language for speed and efficiency. C was a natural environment for writing an operating system. Today, both C and UNIX are available for a wider variety of computer hardware platforms than any other programming language or operating system. This level of portability in computer programming makes UNIX popular even still.

1.1.11.3 THE 1970s

The first microprocessor chip was developed in 1971.Three inventors, Andrew Grove, Robert Noyce, and Gordon Moore founded Intel to produce computer memory chips in 1968. In 1971, the 4004 microprocessor chip, designed by a team under the leadership of Federico Faggin, was introduced to replace the central processing units that heretofore had been constructed from discrete components. The microprocessor chip was born. Intel's later products, from 8080 through 8088 and currently Pentium IV were all descended from the 4004 microprocessor chip.

Back in 1972, music was sold on vinyl records. These records were large platters with spiral grooves cut in them. The music information was stored in the grooves by controlling the depth and direction of the cutting machine. However, the grooves eventually wore, resulting in decreased fidelity. The laserdisc was created by Philips to correct this problem. Instead of grooves, pits were burned into the aluminum surface to represent the 1's and 0's of computer technology. A laser beam either reflected off the spot or was absorbed by the pit. The early laserdiscs were the same size and shape as vinyl records, but they could hold both video and audio on their reflective plastic platter. The information had to be read by a laserdisc player, which was initially expensive. But in time this became a popular medium for home movies.

Figure 1.3 A VINYL RECORD PLAYER

The Motorola microprocessor chip was created in 1974. Motorola's 6800 was the forerunner of the 68000. The 68K was used in the original Macintosh computer system. It provided the computer horsepower to run a graphical user interface, or GUI. Although the Intel microprocessor line would come to dominate desktop computing, the current Apple computer products still use Power PC chips, which are the descendants of this powerful microprocessor chip.

Radio Shack introduces the first pre-built personal computer with built-in keyboard and display. This was the first non-kit personal computer to be marketed to the general public. In 1977, Brad Roberts bought one of these Tandy/Radio Shack computers, known as the trS-80. It came with a simple cassette tape player for loading and saving programs. This allowed Brad to do word processing, using programs like CopyArt. It also produced a revolution in thinking which gradually took hold and gained momentum during the next decade. No longer would the computer be seen as an expensive mathematical tool of large scientific, military, and business institutions, but as a communication and information management tool accessible to everyone.

In 1977, Apple Computer begins delivery of the Apple II computer. The Apple II came fully assembled with a built-in keyboard, monitor and operating system software. The first Apple IIs used a cassette tape to store programs, but a floppy disk drive was soon available. With its ease in storing and running programs, the floppy disk made the Apple II computer the first computer suitable for use in elementary school classrooms.

1.1.11.4 THE 1980s

In 1984, the Apple Macintosh was the first computer to come with a graphical user interface and a mouse pointing device as standard equipment. With the coming of the Mac, the personal microcomputer began to undergo a major revolution in its purpose and use. No longer a tool for just scientists, bankers, and engineers, the microcomputer became the tool of choice for many graphic artists, teachers, instructional designers, librarians, and information managers. Its basic metaphor of a user desktop with its little folders and paper documents hit home with these users, many of whom had never seen a big computer mainframe. The Macintosh would eventually develop standardized symbols for use by humans in communicating with the machine and ultimately contribute to the World Wide Web's metaphor of a virtual world. The Macintosh GUI also paved the way for the development of multimedia applications. The hardware obstacles that prevented hypermedia from becoming a reality were no more.

FIGURE 1.4 FIRST APPLE MACINTOSH COMPUTER

In the Mid-1980s, Artificial Intelligence (AI) developed as a separate discipline from information science. AI is a somewhat broad field that covers many areas. With the development of computer programming involving ever increasing levels of complexity, inheritance, and code re-use culminating in object oriented programming, the software foundations for AI were laid. Other developments in cybernetics, neural networks, and human psychology added their contributions. Some practical but as of yet imperfect implementations of AI include expert systems, Management Information Systems, (MIS), information searching using fuzzy logic, and human speech recognition. Artificial Intelligence today is best defined as a collection of electronic information processing tools that can be applied in a myriad of innovative ways to existing information technologies. Most scientists believe that a machine can never be built to replicate the human mind and emotions, but will be used to do more and more of the tedious labor in finding and presenting the appropriate information in humanity's vast, ever-growing collection of data.

In August of 1987, Apple Computer introduced Hypercard to the public by bundling it with all new Macintosh computers. Hypermedia was a reality at last, with the hardware and software now in place to bring it into being. Hypercard made hypertext document linking possible for the average person who wished to build an information network linking all of his or her electronic documents that could be entered or pasted into a Hypercard stack. Based on the metaphor of index cards in a recipe box, it was easy enough for even young students to use. Yet it was powerful enough to become the software tool used to create the Voyager educational multimedia titles. Hypercard also had provision for displaying graphics and controlling an external device to display video, which would ideally be a laserdisc player.

1.1.11.5 THE 1990s

In 1991, two major commercial events took place which put the power of CD-ROM storage technology and computer based search engines in the hands of ordinary people. World Library Incorporated produced a fully searchable CD-ROM containing 450 (later expanded to 953) classical works of literature and historic documents. This demonstrated the power of the CD-ROM to take the text content of several bookshelves and concentrate it on one small piece of circular plastic. The other product was the electronic version of Grolier's Encyclopedia which actually contained a few pictures in addition to text. Both products were originally marketed through the Bureau of Electronic Publishing, a distributor of CD-ROM products. Many saw this as the ultimate in personal data storage and retrieval. They didn't have to wait long for much greater things in the world of multimedia. Though both titles sold initially for several hundred dollars, by 1994 they could be found at electronic flea markets selling for a dollar or two each. Technological advances had occurred so rapidly in this area that both the Multimedia PC standard and the Macintosh multimedia system extensions made these two products obsolete in a couple of years.

Working together, Motorola, Apple, and IBM developed the Power PC RISC processor to be used in Apple Computer's new Power Macintosh. The product line currently includes the 601, 603, and 604 microprocessors. These chips are designed around a reduced instruction set machine language, intended to produce more compact, faster executing code. Devotees of the Intel CISC chip architecture heartily disagree with this assertion. The result is that the consumer benefits from the intense competition to develop a better computer chip.

The World-Wide Web was introduced by Tim Berners-Lee, with assistance from Robert Caillau (while both were working at CERN). Tim saw the need for a standard linked information system accessible across the range of different computers in use. It had to be simple so that it could work on both dumb terminals and high-end graphical X-Window platforms. He got some pages up and was able to access them with his 'browser'. By 1993, Internet access and usage grew exponentially, as tools become more available and easier to use. People begin referring to the Internet as the information superhighway.

FIGURE 1.5 WORLD-WIDE-WEB SERVERS

On October 24, 1995, the Federal Networking Council (FNC) unanimously passed a resolution defining the term Internet. This definition was developed in consultation with members of the internet and intellectual property rights communities. RESOLUTION: The FNC agrees that the following language reflects our definition of the term "Internet". "Internet" refers to the global information system that -- (i) is logically linked together by a globally unique address space based on the Internet Protocol (IP) or its subsequent extensions/follow-ons; (ii) is able to support communications using the Transmission Control Protocol/Internet Protocol (TCP/IP) suite or its subsequent extensions/follow-ons, and/or other IP-compatible protocols; and (iii) provides, uses or makes accessible, either publicly or privately, high level services layered on the communications and related infrastructure described herein.

Also in 1995, the CDROM Capacity had increased. A handful of CD-ROM disks had the capacity to store all the knowledge and memories of an average person's lifetime.

FIGURE 1.6 CD-ROM

When computers were first built, memory was a precious resource. To conserve memory, dates were stored in a compressed form, utilizing every bit (i.e. single binary digits containing 1 or 0). Not surprisingly, years were stored as two decimal digits, 00 through 99. As the end of the second millennium came, fears arose as to what would happen to computer systems when the new millennium started. Early tests showed that many computers improperly handled the transition from 1999 to the year 2000, so this became known as the Y2K bug. A massive effort was undertaken to avert this doomsday scenario. People feared that planes would fall out of the sky. All computer source code was reviewed, and fixes were designed for the problem areas. Some were band-aids, just offsetting the date by, say, 50 years or so. Others were massive rewrites of source code that had been running successfully for 30 years. Engineers were called out of retirement that had worked on the source code in the 1960s.

1.1.11.6 FIRST DECADE OF THE 21ST CENTURY

On January 1, 2000, everyone held their breath. Although there were some problems, the general population never saw them. The massive Y2K bug worst case scenario had been averted.

The Compact Disc (CD) was by now in every home. But the CD suffered from the fact that it only contained audio or musical information. By 2002, a new medium, known as the Digital Versatile Disc, or DVD, came to the market. The DVD could store video or audio. It had capacity for gigabytes of information, where the CD was limited to megabytes. This technological development made it possible for consumers to buy home movies again. The DVD worked like a laserdisc, reading the pits in the media via a laser beam without making physical contact. Hence, there is virtually no wear and tear on a DVD.

FIGURE 1.7 INTERNAL MECHANISM OF A DVD-ROM DRIVE

Broadband is the name for high capacity interfaces between the home and the public Internet. In 2003, this became readily available in most metropolitan areas of the US. This made it possible for PC users to download files that were megabytes in size in just a few minutes, rather than taking hours over a modem connection. This rapid increase in capacity enabled all sorts of new applications, including musical file sharing.

PCs have always depended on integration of circuits - i.e. the IC chip of 1958. By 2004, new CPU chips combine the processor with new capabilities to process audio and video. The result is a new set of computers with built in support for High Definition Television (HDTV) and 7.1 surround sound. This will further reduce costs while providing even smaller packages.

Blogs became popular in 2005. Blogs are personal web spaces where individuals can share their own thoughts and ideas. Corporations began to incorporate blogs in their networks, allowing employees to use sophisticated web server technology to talk about their work. Unfortunately, sometimes this lead to problems, as employees shared more than they were supposed to; but on the whole, most employees found a new, creative outlet for self-expression.

In 2006, a war between HD DVD and Blu-Ray was in full force. Players and game consoled were introduced for both new high definition video formats. It reminds you of the war between VHS and Beta. But who will win? Only time will tell. However, the winning format promises to capture the DVD market for years to come. So billions are at stake. And the consumer wins in the long run as DVD takes on additional resolution and quality. The amazing thing is that a piece of media using these formats can store at least 30 GB! Still, we are a long way from being able to make computer backups on these media.

By 2007, Blu-Ray had won. Game consoles finally settled down with Blu-Ray winning the format war. Now game developers and players alike can concentrate on the new games that this format allows.

From 2008 on, memory prices continue to come down, enabling smaller and smaller electronic gadgets. Where will it all end? Maybe a postage stamp sized memory circuit to hold all of the memory you will ever need. In actuality, there are researchers at IBM working on just that. Stay tuned.

As of 2009, Smart Phones became more and more popular, as businesses like Apple and Google came on board. In one sense, these devices have become handheld computers, integrating Personal Information Management applications. Besides business applications like email and instant messaging, these phones now provide entertainment. As 3G technologies grow in popularity, data traffic also increases - to the point of being a problem for the main network carriers. The cell phone has become the indispensable device that everyone has and uses everywhere.

FIGURE 1.8 SMART PHONES

As 2010, Social Networking sites really took off in popularity. Who would think that something as simple as uploading a picture to a web site could become so popular? Yet, thousands, even millions are doing just that on sites like Facebook. And others are self-tracking their every move so their friends can find them wherever they are on sites like Twitter.

FIGURE 1.9 SOME POPULAR SOCIAL NETWORK SERVICES

1.1.11.7 SECOND DECADE OF THE 21ST CENTURY

Mobile communication is so integrated into our society that many people feel uncomfortable without a cell phone. Once upon a time, the most popular functions of phones were calling and sending texts. Now smartphones, which are multifunctional devices, are rapidly taking their place of standard cell phones. In addition to communicating, smartphones allow users to learn, earn and have fun. Mobile applications make it possible for smartphones to utilize multiple tasks.

Mobile applications date back to the end of the twentieth century. Typically, they were small arcade games, ring tone editors, calculators, calendars, and so forth. The beginning of the new millennium saw a rapid market evolution of mobile content and applications. Operating systems for smartphones (Windows Mobile, Symbian, RIM, Android, Mac iOS), are open to the development of third-party software, unlike the conventional programming environment of standard cell phones.

Manufacturers tried to make their products more attractive for customers by introducing more and more applications. But quality matters as well. Cell phone development needs to be easy and intuitive. Every company tries to facilitate the process of development so that users are able to customize their devices. Motivation: Juniper Research estimates in 2014 the direct and indirect revenues from sales of mobile applications will total 25 billion dollars.

Mobile users demand more choice, more opportunities to customize their phones and more functionality. Mobile operators want to provide value-added content to their subscribers in a manageable and lucrative way. Mobile developers want the freedom to develop the powerful mobile applications users demand without restrictions. Finally, handset manufacturers want a stable, secure, and affordable platform to power their devices.

In the second decade of the 21st Century, the use of another digital device while watching TV is fairly common. Many people cannot watch a show in its entirety without interacting with another device. They will be checking email, texting, tweeting, pinning, visiting Facebook or hunting for spoilers. Others will be unlocking their smartphones every 60 seconds or casually flipping through content on their tablet or e-reader.

FIGURE 1.10 NETWORK AMC CREATED AN INTERACTIVE APP FOR A SHOW

The Convergence Consulting Group reported that 2.65 million people ditched TV subscriptions for the Web between 2008 and 2011 and furthermore resisted the urge to open a new tab in their browser, just to play along. For many of us, that's far less intuitive than it sounds. Our mobile devices have not only given us a new option when deciding where to watch a favorite show, but they've also changed the way we experience TV. Whereas we simply watched one screen in the era of "The Cosby Show," some of us would be at a loss if we couldn't have our laptops out while also viewing "Modern Family."

Having that "second screen" -- the common phrase for a mobile device used while watching a TV program -- can make us feel like we're being more productive, but it can also broaden our viewing experience. We can figure out what song that "X Factor" contestant performed by searching for lyrics, read a live blog that breaks down issues during a political debate and be vastly entertained while watching reality TV. The Convergence Consulting Group reports that during the second quarter of 2012, 86% of tablet owners and 84% of smartphone owners in the United States said they used their second screen of choice while simultaneously watching TV at least once during a 30-day period. But for 41% of tablet owners and 39% of those owning smartphones, multitasking is more like once a day, at a minimum.

Our attachment to our mobile devices during TV time isn't surprising, least of all to the digital strategists at the networks creating what we view. Some of them, too, have noticed their own propensity to have another device close by while watching TV, which caused them to notice something else: An opportunity. Major broadcast networks and cable programmers alike are tinkering around with what they can offer a second screen captivated audience, as are companies like GetGlue, Miso, Yap.tv and Yahoo's! IntoNow.

While cable programmers are focusing on creating opportunities for engagement across a wide spectrum of shows to serve TV's fan bases, networks are zeroing in on how they can take advantage of their insider knowledge to keep users interacting with them on those inescapable second screens. The Convergence Consulting Group found in a 2011 report that 61% of tablet owners were emailing while also watching a TV show. That's why TV fans are frequently coming across applications pegged as "second screen experiences" -- downloadable environments where viewers can often interact with and learn more about what they're watching on TV, in some cases syncing the application with the TV show.

The second screen seems to work particularly well with live events, as well as reality programming, sporting events and news. For example, Albert Cheng, chief product officer and the executive vice president of digital media for Disney/ABC Television, said ABC saw success with their Backstage Pass app for the Oscars, which offered "all-access" to viewers above and beyond what they could see at any one time on their television screens.

So if you were a fan of 2012's best supporting actress winner Octavia Spencer, Albert Cheng said, "You followed her nomination, you followed her through the red carpet, and when you saw her on TV get her Oscar... with your iPad or computer, you could see her walk down the winners walk and [be interviewed.] ... As a fan, you felt as though you were with her all the way through."

1.2 CAREER CHOICES IN TECHNOLOGIES

Some of the most popular careers in technology are Information Technology (IT), Computer Engineering (CET), Biomedical Technology and Occupational Safety and Health Technology, Environmental Technology, Graphic Communications, CAD Drafting and Computer, Civil Engineering Technology, Chemical Engineering Technology, Medical Technology, and Mechanical Engineering Technology.

.

FIGURE 1.11

1.2.1 DIFFERENCE AMONG SCIENTISTS, ENGINEERS, TECHNOLOGISTS, AND TECHNICIANS

Science is knowledge or understanding about a subject or phenomenon of natural world. Furthermore, science is the understanding and continuous exploration of the natural world. It is a knowledge based upon logic and experimentation that is verifiable. Example of science would be study of Nuclear Physics. A *scientist* in a broad sense is one engaging in a systematic activity to acquire knowledge.

Engineering technicians solve technical problems. Some help engineers and scientists do research and development. They build or set up equipment. They do experiments. They collect data and calculate results. They might also help to make a model of new equipment. Some technicians work in quality control where they check products, do tests, and collect data. In manufacturing, they help to design and develop products. They also find ways to produce things efficiently.

Most technicians focus on one type of engineering, such as civil engineering. They help engineers to plan bridges and roads. They might also get data about traffic. Other technicians focus on electrical engineering. They help to design or test electronics. Other types of engineering technicians work in aerospace, environmental, industrial, or mechanical engineering. Most engineering technicians work about 40 hours a week. They work in labs, offices, factories, or on construction sites. Some might be exposed to dangerous materials.

Engineering and technology are intertwined terms in society. Both the engineer and the technologist use technology, however they use it differently. To understand the difference between engineering and technology, one needs to know what their meaning is. While engineering is a field of study, technology is application based upon science and/or engineering. Furthermore, engineering is applying the outcome of technology to design, develop, and

23

manufacture the end product. To make a long story short, engineers use technology to create something new and technologists use technology to improve something already in existence.

Engineering is both a field of study as well as application of knowledge (scientific) to create or produce something such as products and something structural. Engineering is practiced through the creation of a new facility, machinery or establishment to produce goods, materials and life needs. That is, engineers develop devices that serve practical purposes. If some principles and methods of a science subject such as Nuclear Physics are used to make a structure such as a nuclear reactor, the reactor would be called an example of engineering.

Engineering is a discipline of study that imparts scientific knowledge of designing and building structures, machines, materials, systems and processes as well as application of this knowledge for production of all such categories. Engineering is the process of putting things together to get a desired outcome. When we use the word engineering college, we mean a place where different streams of engineering are taught to students who later qualify to work as engineers in different sectors of economy. Graduates of engineering programs apply scientific concepts to develop solutions to real world problems. Engineering jobs are more theoretical, involving the design of new products or concepts. Some job functions of an engineer might include the following:

- Design
- Development
- Testing
- Research
- Technical Support
- Production
- Analysis

For instance, a design engineer (with the aid of computer design software) might be responsible for designing a part or component for a product. This would involve creating very detailed specifications of the component. The design engineer would also be responsible for testing the component for reliability and safety, making any adjustments or corrections that are needed. The design engineer not only designs products, but in many instances they recreate designs of products that have not performed according to the specified standards.

Engineers work in a variety of business environments, and solve all sorts of complex problems every day. So what kind of a person makes a good engineer? They must be creative, and have good problem solving skills. They must have a good understanding of mathematics and science, computers, and developing technology. Since almost all engineering projects are done by teams, they need good communication skills and leadership qualities. They must be aware of the environmental impact of their work, as well as the needs and desires of the public. Finally, engineers need a good understanding of business practices, finance, and management.

The word technology is commonly used in processes where our knowledge of science and/or engineering is used to control and adapt to our environments. The term technology was first used to describe the ability of human beings to convert natural resources into tools for use. Technology is also an application of knowledge gained through science and/or engineering fields to make or produce complex structures. Examples of technology would be parts of latest appliances and complex applications. Technologists work with technology that already exists. Technologists apply the outcome of scientific principles to innovate and improve man-made things in the world.

Some job functions of the technologist may include the following:

- Identifying equipment needs for businesses
- Supervision of equipment installation
- Analyzing equipment for specific functions
- Development of a manufacturing procedure based on new technology
- Supervision of construction and appropriate building materials

Engineering technology deals with the same topics as engineering, but in a more applied fashion rather than a purely theoretical fashion. Engineering Technology is more concerned with manufacturing, production, and quality control. The mathematics and basic sciences as well as the technical courses in technology programs are taught with more applications and less theory than the related engineering courses. Although engineering technology courses are often less math-intensive, they also include a much higher concentration of laboratory work. Engineering courses also typically require a higher level of mathematics and basic sciences and prepare a student to continue studies and perform research at the graduate levels. Engineering requires at least the full calculus sequence (three courses) and differential equations (some programs require linear algebra also). Engineering Technology requires at least the first calculus course (sometimes two). Technical courses generally have labs associated with the courses that require "hands-on" applications or projects for the topics being studied. For example, graduates from the Civil Engineering Technology bachelor-degree program who desire to continue their studies at the graduate level may be required to take "bridge" course work at some colleges and universities to transition to the higher levels of mathematics and basic sciences required for research and advanced study.

Engineering technologists (ETs) differ from engineering technicians. Technicians generally have an associate degree and usually serve in subordinate roles to technologists, setting up, testing and repairing equipment, as well as performing maintenance and inspections of equipment. ETs have bachelor's or master's degrees. A general engineering technologist degree prepares ETs to work in a variety of disciplines and in various work environments. Not all engineering technology degrees are accredited by the Accreditation Board for Engineering and Technologies (ABET), so make sure to do research before committing to a school. Many ET programs are regionally accredited. With a general ET degree, you can apply for many jobs that require engineering technology backgrounds, even if you don't have specialized training in that discipline. Hands-on training or further classroom training may be required. Working outside on job sites, spending your days in manufacturing or industrial plants, or working in a laboratory setting all are possibilities.

The Accreditation Board for Engineering and Technology (ABET) sets guidelines for what defines engineering, engineering technologist, and engineering technician educational degree programs. While it may seem elitist to distinguish engineering and engineering technology, there are technical and legal reasons for so doing. Engineering normally involves detailed analysis and design that results in the creation of machines, structures, processes, materials, and information for the benefit of society. Engineers bear responsibility for their creations through professional registration which is regulated by each state. The first step in this registration process is to earn a bachelor of science degree in engineering from an ABET-accredited college of engineering. Also, engineering graduates may take the first part of the Professional Engineer's Exam immediately upon graduation. Engineering Technologists may not.

Both engineering and technology affect society and human life in general. It is through the use of engineering and technology that a nation makes use of its natural resources. These two are indispensable for growth of infrastructure and economic development of any nation. Leaps in science, engineering and technology help in advancement and betterment of human life and are invaluable in saving humanity from many natural and man-made disasters as well.

TABLE 1.1 THE INDUSTRIAL TEAM—DUTIES AND EDUCATION

Duties	%Theory	% Applied	Education Required/Degree
Scientist—hypothesizes and verifies laws of nature	90	10	Five to seven years of college M.S. or Ph.D.
Engineer—designs and creates hardware and software from scientific ideas and laws of nature	70	30	Four or five years of college B.S. or M.S.
Technologist—makes design prototype, suggests redesign or modification, acts as manufacturing engineer	60	40	Four years of college B.S.E.T.
Technician—makes model of prototype, tests and troubleshoots prototypes and hardware/software in actual production use, acts as manufacturing supervisor	50	50	Two years of college A.S.E.T.
Skilled worker (craftsperson)—produces parts (e.g., holding fixtures) from completed designs, installs and runs hardware	20	80	Four years of on-the-job training (OJT) and/or vocational high school High school diploma and training/experience

Table 1.1 illustrates the members of the industrial team implemented by most corporate infrastructures. The percentages for theory and hands-on experience in college are provided. M.S. stands for Masters of Science. PhD. Represents Doctor of Philosophy. B.S.E.T. is the acronym for Bachelor of Science in Engineering Technology. A.S.E.T. is the acronym for Associate of Science in Engineering Technology.

1.2.2 CAREER CHOICES IN INFORMATION TECHNOLOGY

Information Technology (IT) is an area within engineering that focuses on using computers to store, transmit and communicate information. Every computer database and network is developed and maintained by information technology professionals. Individuals who enjoy math and working on computers should consider a career in information technology because job growth is expected to be much faster than average in this field from 2008 to 2018.

1.2.2.1 COMPUTER SUPPORT SPECIALIST

Computer support specialists provide technical assistance and advice to individuals within organizations on how to use computer systems, software and hardware. In addition, computer support specialists are responsible for running diagnostic programs to solve problems within a company's computer network. Computer support specialists also oversee the daily performance of company computer systems and make sure they're working properly. The median salary for computer support specialists in the United States in 2014 was $43,450, according to the Bureau of Labor Statistics.

1.2.2.2 COMPUTER SOFTWARE ENGINEER

Computer software engineers use math and computer science to develop computer software for companies. The majority of computer software engineers hold a minimum of a bachelor's degree in computer science. The median salary for computer software engineers in 2014 in the United States was $87,900, according to the Bureau of Labor Statistics.

1.2.2.3 COMPUTER NETWORK ARCHITECT

Computer network architects are responsible for designing new computer networks such as local area networks, Internet networks, wide area networks, and data communications systems. Network architects have to use both computer software and hardware to set up networks. For example, setting up a new network may require the installation of routers (hardware) and the installation of software such as network drivers. The median salary for computer network architects in the United States in 2014 was approximately $71,100, according to the Bureau of Labor Statistics.

1.2.2.4 COMPUTER SYSTEMS ANALYSTS

Computer systems analysts help develop and design new computer systems for companies. Their job involves selecting different computer software and hardware to use within each new system. In addition, computer systems analysts commonly analyze existing computer systems and look for ways to make them more efficient. In the United States, the median salary for computer systems analysts in 2014 was $75,500, according to the Bureau of Labor Statistics.

1.2.2.5 COMPUTER AND INFORMATION SYSTEMS MANAGERS

Computer and information systems managers help coordinate the use of computers within organizations. They speak to other executives within the organization and come up with a plan to help meet the organization's goals with the use of computers. In addition, computer and information systems managers are responsible for overseeing technical tasks within an organization, such as software development and network security. In the United States, the median salary for computer and information systems managers in 2014 was $112,210, according to the Bureau of Labor Statistics.

1.2.3 CAREER CHOICES IN COMPUTER ENGINEERING TECHNOLOGY (CET)

Individuals, who are trained to set up computers, troubleshoot programs and test software fill computer engineering technology jobs. Computer engineers can also write and design software and programs. Computer engineers earn a bachelor's degree in computer software engineering and technology. They may also choose to pursue specialized certifications, from companies such as Microsoft or Cisco, which makes them more valuable as workers in certain environments. The average computer systems software engineer makes between $73,200 and $113,960, according to the U.S. Bureau of Labor Statistics in May 2014. Forbes reports that engineers with 10 to 20 years of experience can earn about 55 to 60 percent more than entry-level workers. The Bureau of Labor Statistics states that 15 percent of all computer engineers worked more than 50 hours per week in 2008, due to the nature of the job. Engineers often face strict deadlines and must complete their work in a hurry. Engineers frequently work as members of a team, which makes meeting deadlines simpler.

Computer Engineering Technology (CET) program is an engineering type program. This means that the CET class material has its roots in science. The CET graduate is concerned with the physical aspects of the computer and the system it is involved with. This type of person should be able to assist in the design and maintenance of one-of-a-kind systems. In comparison, Computer Information Systems (CIS) and Networking Technology (NT) are normally business based and deal primarily with software products, networking equipment, system maintenance and other business-related applications.

Computer engineering careers can be a great choice for new college graduates, as well as older workers who are seeking a better-paying and more stable career path. From computer programmers and network administrators to database administrators and computer support technicians, the U.S. Bureau of Labor Statistics (BLS) reports that job growth for most occupations in this field will be "much faster than average" for professionals who know how to write code, troubleshoot computers and maintain complicated software packages.

Network systems and data communications analysts are projected to be the second-fastest-growing occupation in 2012, according to the Bureau of Labor Statistics. They earn, on average,

$76,560 a year, but the position usually requires on-the-job training or a bachelor's degree. Growth industries: Computer Systems Design and Related Services, Wired Telecommunications Carriers. Growth areas: Virginia, District of Columbia.

FIGURE 1.12

Perhaps one of the most attractive aspects of a career in computer engineering is the salary. According to the BLS, the average salary for computer professionals in 2008 was about $35 per hour, or more than $70,000 per year. This salary makes computer professionals among the highest-paid U.S. employees, as the average salary for all occupations in 2008 was just over $20 per hour, or $42,270 per year.

Some computer-related jobs require only a high school diploma, while others are only available to people with a bachelor's or even a master's degree. According to the BLS, some firms will train high school graduates with certifications in software packages---which are considered to be "the industry standard"---to administer networks and build databases, while others might not consider an applicant who doesn't have a college education. Even people with non-technology related degrees can find jobs in this industry, the BLS says, as many employers view four years of college as a sign that an individual knows how to do research and how to get the answers she or he needs.

The job of a computer professional will vary according to the type of job and the type of company. Computer programmers will be spending much of their time writing code. In some cases, those programmers will be writing brand-new programs, but more often they will be adapting programs that were written by others.

Database administrators are tasked with creating new databases using platforms such as SQL Server and Oracle. Those computer professionals will also spend time troubleshooting databases when things go wrong and optimizing existing databases to make them faster and easier to use.

While the job prospects for those with computer skills are quite strong, not all positions are full time or long term. According to the BLS, many employees in computer engineering roles are self-employed or work on a contract basis. Such roles become available when a company merely needs its network infrastructure established, but doesn't need a full staff once it's up and running. "Such jobs may last from several months to two years or more," the BLS says. Consultants may also be brought in to train staff for upcoming software changes. While such jobs can offer lucrative pay, they seldom come with benefits such as health insurance or vacation time, and can lead to periods of unemployment.

Not all jobs in the computer field will see the same level of growth. In recent years, headlines have screamed about companies outsourcing their help desk services and computer support positions to low-cost countries such as India and China. In fact, according to a 2006 report in The New York Times, public perception of declining jobs in the field has led to fewer students majoring in computer science. Choosing a career that is difficult to outsource can boost your job prospects enormously. Hardware support is a good example of a job that cannot move abroad: Technicians must be available, in-person, to replace failed hardware.

Careers you can get with this degree:

- Computer Systems Engineer
- Computer Systems Security Engineer
- Hardware Design Engineer

1.2.4 CAREER CHOICES IN BIOMEDICAL TECHNOLOGY

Biomedical technology is the application of technology and engineering to living organisms, which can involve a range of activities from designing medical equipment or conducting research. Keep reading to find out more about biomedical technology and about your educational options within this field. Biomedical technology is a broad term that combines engineering and technology to solve biological or medical problems involving humans, especially the design and use of medical equipment used to diagnose and treat various diseases. Biomedical technology can also be broken down into smaller sub-fields:

a) Biomedical Informatics

Biomedical informatics is the branch of biomedical technology that deals with the tracking and measuring of biomedical data by using computers and technology. As a biomedical technician, you'd use the information they gather to better understand different issues, such as how diseases spread or how well health systems are performing.

b) Biomedical Engineering

The branch of biomedical technology concerned with the application of engineering design and principles to medical and biological issues is called biomedical engineering. Your work as a biomedical engineer would involve developing and growing synthetic organs or creating prosthetic limbs to replace diseased or injured parts of the human body.

c) Biomedical Research

Biomedical research is the study of various chemicals and substances used to develop and improve medicines that are used to treat disease. The research is often conducted using equipment and methods developed by people working in other branches of biomedical technology.

d) Biomedical Science

Biomedical science, also known as health science, is the application of chemistry, biology, physics, engineering and other scientific disciplines to the research and treatment of human health issues. Biomedical technology and biomedical science overlap in many aspects, but as a biomedical scientist, you'd focus more on the actual research and treatment of disease, while as a biomedical technician, you'd deal more with researching and developing technologies and methodologies used to treat disease.

The work carried out in a medical laboratory is divided mainly into four categories, namely diagnostic work, blood transfusion technology, research and the preparation of serums and vaccines. Diagnostic work however forms the major part of biomedical technologists' work and include the following five disciplines:

a) Haematology

This is the study of blood (Chemical pathology)
This entails the chemical analyses of body fluids such as blood and urine.

b) Histopathology

This is the study of diseases that affect body tissues, for example cancer and any other change in the cells of organs that interfere with normal function.

c) Microbiology

This is the study of bacteria, fungi and viruses that can cause diseases.

Cytology

Cytology is the analyzing of cells that the body normally exfoliates.
In the field of blood transfusion technology, biomedical technologists perform the necessary tests on donated blood. This includes for example the identification of blood groups and antibodies. Blood is also tested for various diseases like aids and hepatitis.

FIGURE 1.13 ULTRASOUND REPRESENTATION OF URNARY BLADDER

An extensive classification and registration system is used in every medical laboratory to ensure that specimens do not get misplaced or exchanged. Biomedical technologists must keep reports of the test results and ensure that these are available for years to come. Most medical laboratories are connected to hospitals in the bigger centers of our country and they are generally equipped with modern and sophisticated analytical instruments and microscopes. Due to the danger of working with infected material, all laboratories must conform to certain safety regulations at all times. Every specimen must be handled as if it is a source of serious infection. In laboratories offering a twenty-four hour service, biomedical technologists are expected to do after-hours emergency work, which might include night and weekend work.

 Biomedical technologists must be neat, careful and methodical persons. Accuracy is of the utmost importance in the work as negligence could endanger patients' lives. A high concentration capacity is essential. Biomedical technologists are expected to give their undivided attention to their work so that even a slight variation or change in an experiment will not go unnoticed. All members of this medical profession must be extremely responsible and adhere strictly to the professional code of ethics. For example, no information of laboratory findings may be made known to the public except where ethical procedures allow it.

Biomedical technologists are employed by state laboratories, Institute for Medical Research, pathology departments at universities and private pathologists. After a two-year period of practicing as biomedical technologists, these professionals can apply to the Interim National Medical and Dental Council to practice privately. Biomedical technologists can work for themselves or enter into group practices with medical doctors.

Undergraduate degree programs in biomedical technology, or biomedical engineering, can be found at the associate's and bachelor's degree levels. Associate's degree programs typically focus on teaching you how to use, install and repair equipment found in hospitals and other health care facilities. Bachelor's degree programs typically offer coursework that covers a variety of topics, such as laboratory analysis procedures used to diagnose diseases and testing methods used by pharmaceutical companies, among other topics.

Graduate degree programs are available at the master's and doctoral degree levels. You can pursue graduate degrees in biomedical technology and biomedical engineering. These programs are typically designed to prepare graduates for careers at public and private research facilities, academic institutions or manufacturing settings. Most graduate programs in this field also offer the opportunity to specialize in specific areas, such as bio-imaging, nanotechnology and tissue engineering.

1.2.5 CAREER CHOICES IN OCCUPATIONAL SAFETY AND HEALTH TECHNOLOGY

Occupational safety and health technology programs prepare people to help safety engineers maintain health and safety standards in the workplace. Students learn principles of engineering. They also learn to inspect and monitor worksites. They learn to test samples in labs. Some threats to safety and health in the workplace are obvious. Police officers often can tell when they are getting into a dangerous situation. Lumberjacks can see the enormous bulk of a tree as it falls and know they have to keep their distance. But other hazards are not so obvious. At one time, workers used to paint radioactive materials onto clock parts to make the dials glow in the dark. Only when workers started getting sick did people realize that radioactivity can be a workplace health hazard. Similar discoveries have been made about airborne cotton fibers in fabric mills. Some scientists have raised an alarm about the solvent used in some liquid-paper products. Is this a real threat or a trivial matter? Experts in occupational safety and health technology do research that answers such questions. Some of these experts are engineers, but others are technologists and technicians who work as part of the engineering team.

You can study this field at several levels. You can prepare to be a technician by studying full time for two years beyond high school. This earns you an associate degree. About 45 colleges offer a program of this kind. You learn how to evaluate conditions in the workplace by evaluating chemical, biological, and physical hazards. To do so, you need to be good at these sciences and the math that accompanies them. You study statistics so that you can interpret the data you collect and reach good conclusions. You also learn how to use proper equipment for

33

personal protection, decontamination, calibration, and measurement. And you study how to handle hazardous situations such as chemical spills, prepare hazardous wastes for transport, and prevent fires.

FIGURE 1.14 AN OCCUPATIONAL HEALTH AND SAFETY TECHNICIAN PREPARING AND CALIBRATING SCIENTIFIC EQUIPMENT

You can enter the field at a higher level of responsibility if you earn a bachelor's degree by studying for four years beyond high school. About 30 colleges offer this degree. You usually need this degree to apply for certification with a professional association. Experience in the field is also usually required. Certification is not required by law, but it opens up job opportunities.

A four-year program is likely to give you greater depth in science and math than a two-year program. It is also more likely to include supervised work experience, which can be valuable for teaching you skills and also for making professional contacts that will be useful when you enter the job market.

If you plan on the bachelor's, you should look for a program that has a good helping of science, math, and engineering subjects. (Look for 60 or more semester hours, with at least 15 at the upper-division level.) The five or so programs approved by the Accreditation Board for Science and Technology (ABET) all meet this standard. This kind of program prepares you to design large, complex strategies for assessing exposure to hazards. It also meets the entry requirements for graduate school in this field.

Graduate school is yet another way of entering the work force. You may earn a bachelor's in occupational safety and health technology or in some other field of science, math, or engineering, then a master's degree in this field. This takes a year or two beyond the bachelor's. The roughly 20 ABET-approved programs will give you an especially good background in the science and technology.

You can prepare for this program by taking courses in high school that prepare you for college. This typically includes four years of English, three years of math, three years of social studies, and two years of science. Some colleges also require two years of a second language.

Classes to take in high school:

- Computer Science and Programming
- English Composition
- Biology
- Chemistry
- Physics
- Trigonometry

Admission to graduate programs is competitive. You need a bachelor's degree in a relevant field (science, math, or engineering), good grades, and good test scores. Your math skills should include calculus, and you should have some background in statistics. You need good communications skills to succeed in this field. A writing course, and probably a public speaking course, should be part of your program even if they are not required. Consider taking some business courses. You are going to work closely with management, so you need to be able to speak that language. In addition, the skills you learn in these courses may later help you make a career shift into management.

Additional requirements at some schools include:

- Graduate Record Exam (GRE) General
- Graduate Record Exam (GRE) Biology, Chemistry
- Letters of recommendation

An associate degree program in this field typically includes courses in the following subjects:

- College Algebra
- College Trigonometry
- Elementary Statistics
- Engineering Technology Economics
- English Composition
- Fire Prevention and Protection
- General Chemistry
- General Physics
- Hazardous Material Management
- Human Anatomy and Physiology
- Industrial Hygiene
- Industrial Toxicology

- Introduction to Computer Science
- Safety Engineering and Technology

A bachelor's degree program often assumes that you have taken most of the math courses listed above while in high school. It typically includes the other courses listed above, plus the following:

- Calculus
- Epidemiology
- General Biology
- Industrial Ergonomics
- Industrial Safety
- Introduction to Microcomputers
- Microbiology
- Occupational Health Law
- Organic Chemistry
- Radiological Health
- Supervised work experience or internship

A master's degree program includes courses similar to those listed for the bachelor's, but you are more likely to specialize in one of those subjects. It typically includes the following:

- Required courses
- Thesis or project
- Internship (may not be required)

Similar fields of study:

- Applied Mathematics
- Biological Sciences, General
- Chemical Technology
- Chemistry
- Computational Mathematics
- Engineering Technology, General
- Environmental Health
- Mathematics
- Occupational Safety and Health
- Physical Sciences, General
- Statistics

Careers you may qualify for:

- Engineering Technicians
- Occupational Health and Safety Specialists
- Science Technicians

1.2.6 CAREER CHOICES IN ENVIRONMENTAL TECHNOLOGY

Can you imagine if the kitchen in your house never got cleaned? Eventually the rotting food and dirty dishes would create a very unpleasant and physically unsafe environment in which to live. It is the job of environmental technologists and technicians to ensure that we live in as clean an environment as possible. This involves collecting information regarding the presence and effects of pollutants in our air, water and soil. Environmental technologists and technicians have a comprehensive knowledge of waste reduction, management methods and issues. They are capable of data handling and acquisition using computer software. Environmental technology (abbreviated as envirotech) or green technology (abbreviated as greentech) or clean technology (abbreviated as cleantech) is the application of one or more of environmental science, green chemistry, environmental monitoring and electronic devices to monitor, model and conserve the natural environment and resources, and to curb the negative impacts of human involvement.

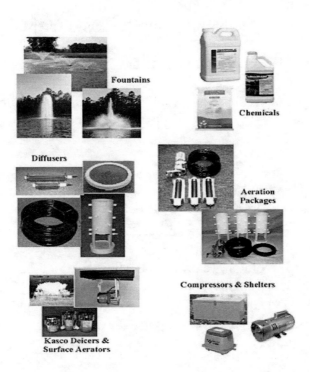

FIGURE 1.15 ENVIRONMENTAL TECHNOLOGIES

Some specific duties of technologists and technicians would include:

- Field sampling: air, water and soil

- Solid, liquid and air treatment methods and waste minimization

- Hazardous goods and waste handling methods

- WHMIS (Workplace Hazardous Management Information Systems) implementation and compliance evaluation

- Emergency planning and spill response methods

- Recycling and waste minimization program design

- Environmental issue analysis and environmental law and ethics

- Developing and implementing air, water or soil quality measurement plans

- Taking inventory of and quantifying sources of locally-generated pollution

- Using different laboratory techniques and instruments to prepare and analyze samples

- Preparing reports of lab results for internal and external use

- Responding to complaints about air, water or soil quality from community members

Career Options:

- Air monitoring consultant;
- Conservation authority;
- Chemical production and processing (e.g. process control, quality control inspection, etc.);
- Environmental and engineering consulting firm;
- Government agency and laboratory (e.g. Ontario Ministry of the Environment, Ontario Ministry Energy, local municipalities, etc.);
- Industrial laboratory (e.g. quality control labs or analytical labs); and
- Scientific equipment sales and technical support.

Where Will You Work?

As an environmental technologist or technician, you might find yourself working for the provincial or federal government, or for private industry. If you work for private industry, you may find yourself working for environmental labs, consulting firms, pulp and paper mills, chemical refineries or utility companies.

You will work both indoors and outdoors, and normally work a regular Monday to Friday work week, with occasional overtime. You will work in lab environments and be exposed to toxic materials so you must be trained and knowledgeable in safety measures.

How Much Will You Earn?

- Technologist: $55,000 - $70,000/yr.
- Technician: $54,000 - $60,000/yr.

How Does the Future Look?

Public and government awareness of environmental issues has greatly expanded the roles of environmental technologists and technicians. The job prospects for this field are expected to remain good-to-excellent over the next 10 years.

How Can You Get Started?

In high school, be sure to take courses in English, Math, Physics, Chemistry and Biology.

What Will You Need?

To be a successful environmental technologist or technician you should enjoy the outdoors and have a passion to improve the quality of the environment. You need to be analytical, efficient, research-oriented, good oral communications, good written communications and be able to manage your time well.

1.2.6.1 CAREER CHOICES IN ENVIRONMENTAL ENGINEERING TECHNOLOGY

Working with environmental engineers, environmental Engineering Technologists (ETs) develop techniques and equipment to analyze, control and prevent environmental hazards. Inspection, maintenance and repair of equipment may be involved in the areas of air pollution, water pollution, hazardous materials, recycling and waste management. Fields of specialty can vary, as can work environments. Possibilities include environmental and safety management, regulatory compliance, and chemical manufacturing, be it outdoors or indoors. The government employs many environmental engineering technologists at waste and wastewater treatment plants, in watershed protection programs, in air and water pollution control, regulation and enforcement, and as regulatory compliance officers.

1.2.6.2 TOP TEN EMERGING ENVIRONMENTAL TECHNOLOGIES

Wasteful energy policies, overuse of resources, water supply shortages, global climate change, and deforestation are just some of the issues experts say need to be addressed for humans to achieve sustainable living on this planet. By the year 2025, an additional 2.9 billion people will strain tightening water supplies, and the world's energy needs will go up 60 percent by 2030, according to the United Nations.

FIGURE 1.16

1.2.6.2.1 MAKE OIL FROM JUST ABOUT ANYTHING

Any carbon-based waste, from turkey guts to used tires, can, by adding sufficient heat and pressure, be turned into oil through a process called thermo-depolymerization, This is very similar to how nature produces oil, but with this technology, the process is expedited by millions of years to achieve the same byproduct. Proponents of this technology claim that a ton of turkey waste can cough up about 600 pounds of petroleum.

FIGURE 1.17

1.2.6.2.2 REMOVE THE SALT

According to the United Nations, water supply shortages will affect billions of people by the middle of this century. Desalination, basically removing the salt and minerals out of seawater, is one way to provide potable water in parts of the world where supplies are limited. The problem with this technology is that it is expensive and uses a lot of energy. Scientists are working toward better processes where inexpensive fuels can heat and evaporate the water before running it through membranes with microscopic pores to increase efficiency.

FIGURE 1.18

1.2.6.2.3 THE 'H' POWER

Hydrogen fuel cell usage has been touted as a pollution-free alternative to using fossil fuels. They make water by combining hydrogen and oxygen. In the process, they generate electricity. The problem with fuel cells is obtaining the hydrogen. Molecules such as water and alcohol have to be processed to extract hydrogen to feed into a fuel cell. Some of these processes require the use of other energy sources, which then defeat the advantages of this "clean" fuel. Most recently, scientists have come up with ways to power laptops and small devices with fuel cells, and some car companies are promising that soon we'll be seeing cars that emit nothing but clean water. The promise of a "hydrogen economy," however, is not one that all experts agree will ever be realized. Figure 1.18 shows the Chevy Equinox Fuel cell, which runs on hydrogen and emits only water.

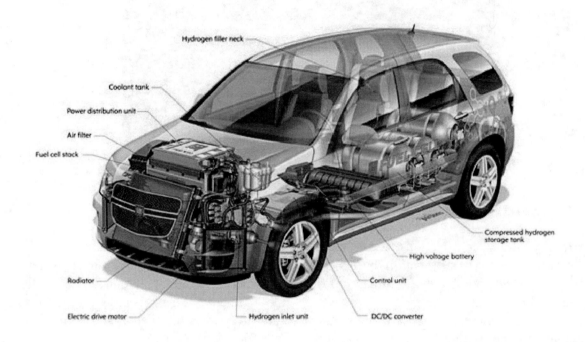

FIGURE 1.19

1.2.6.2.4 SUNNY NEW IDEAS

The sun's energy, which hits Earth in the form of photons, can be converted into electricity or heat. Solar collectors come in many different forms and are already used successfully by energy companies and individual homeowners. The two widely known types of solar collectors are solar cells and solar thermal collectors. But researchers are pushing the limits to more efficiently convert this energy by concentrating solar power by using mirrors and parabolic dishes. Part of the challenge for employing solar power involves motivation and incentives from governments. In January, the state of California approved a comprehensive program that provides incentives toward solar development. Arizona, on the other hand, has ample sunshine but has not made solar energy a priority. In fact in some planned communities it is downright discouraged by strict rules of aesthetics.

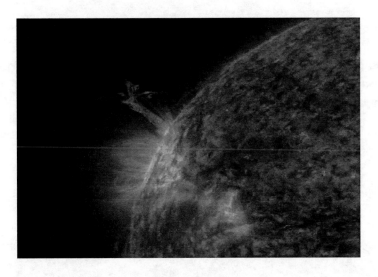

FIGURE 1.20

1.2.6.2.5 OCEAN THERMAL ENERGY CONVERSION

The biggest solar collector on Earth is our ocean mass. According to the U.S. Department of Energy, the oceans absorb enough heat from the sun to equal the thermal energy contained in 250 billion barrels of oil each day. The U.S. consumes about 7.5 billion barrels a year. OTEC technologies convert the thermal energy contained in the oceans and turn it into electricity by using the temperature difference between the water's surface, which is heated, and the cold of the ocean's bottom. This difference in temperature can operate turbines that can drive generators. The major shortcoming of this technology is that it's still not efficient enough to be used as a major mechanism for generating power.

FIGURE 1.21

1.2.6.2.6 HARNESS WAVES AND TIDES

The oceans cover more than 70 percent of the Earth's surface. Waves contain an abundance of energy that could be directed to turbines, which can then turn this mechanical power into electrical. The obstacle to using this energy source has been the difficulty in harnessing it.

Sometimes the waves are too small to generate sufficient power. The trick is to be able to store the energy when enough mechanical power is generated. New York City's East River is now in the process of becoming the test bed for six tide-powered turbines, and Portugal's reliance on waves in a new project is expected to produce enough power for more than 1,500 homes. In Figure 1.21, a Wavebob, a buoy system, captures the ocean's power.

FIGURE 1.22

1.2.6.2.7 PLANT YOUR ROOF

It's a wonder that this concept attributed to the Hanging Gardens of Babylon, one of Seven Wonders of the World, didn't catch on sooner in the modern world. Legend has it that the roofs, balconies, and terraces of the royal palace of Babylon were turned into gardens by the king's order to cheer up one of his wives. Roof gardens help absorb heat, reduce the carbon dioxide impact by taking up CO_2 and giving off oxygen, absorb storm water, and reduce summer air conditioning usage. Ultimately, the technique could lessen the "heat island" effect that occurs in urban centers. Butterflies and songbirds could also start frequenting urban garden roofs, and like the king's wife, could even cheer up the inhabitants of the building. In Figure 1.22, a green roof is tested at Chicago's City Hall.

FIGURE 1.23

1.2.6.2.8 LET PLANTS AND MICROBES CLEAN UP AFTER US

Bioremediation uses microbes and plants to clean up contamination. Examples include the cleanup of nitrates in contaminated water with the help of microbes, and using plants to uptake arsenic from contaminated soil (like the Arabidopsis in Figure 1.23), in a process known as phytoremediation. The U.S. Environmental Protection Agency has used it to clean up several sites. Often, native plant species can be used for site cleanup, which are advantageous because in most cases they don't require pesticides or watering. In other cases scientists are trying to genetically modify the plants to take up contaminants in their roots and transport it all the way to the leaves for easy harvesting.

FIGURE 1.24

1.2.6.2.9 BURY THE BAD STUFF

Carbon dioxide is the most prominent greenhouse gas contributing to global warming. According to the Energy Information Administration, by the year 2030 we will be emitting close to 8,000 million metric tons of CO_2. Some experts say it's impossible to curb the emission of CO_2 into the atmosphere and that we just have to find ways to dispose of the gas. One suggested method is to inject it into the ground before it gets a chance to reach the atmosphere. After the CO_2 is separated from other emission gases, it can be buried in abandoned oil wells, saline reservoirs, and rocks. While these sounds great, scientists are not sure whether the injected gas will stay underground and what the long-term effects are and the costs of separation and burying are still far too high to consider this technology as a practical short-term solution.

FIGURE 1.25

1.2.6.2.10 MAKE PAPER OBSOLETE

Imagine curling up on the couch with the morning paper and then using the same sheet of paper to read the latest novel by your favorite author. That's one possibility of electronic paper, a flexible display that looks very much like real paper but can be reused over and over. The display contains many tiny microcapsules filled with particles that carry electric charges bonded to a steel foil. Each microcapsule has white and black particles that are associated with either a positive or negative charge. Depending on which charge is applied; the black or white particles surface displaying different patterns. In the United States alone, more than 55 million newspapers are sold each weekday.

FIGURE 1.26

1.2.7 CAREER CHOICES IN GRAPHICS COMMUNICATION

The graphic communication industry started as the printing and publishing business. After rapid technological advances with electronic media, the printing business evolved into the graphic communications industry. According to the California Polytechnic State University's Graphic Communication Department, the industry "includes electronic and traditional printing, publishing, packaging, digital imaging, computer graphics, website development, digital photography, printable electronics and related areas." The design work applies to mass communications and media for marketing, packaging, advertising, websites, newspapers, books and more. According to the Pennsylvania College of Technology, the graphic communications industry is the fourth largest industry in the United States. The graphics communication industry requires continuous learning with the new computer and software as shown in Figure 1.26.

FIGURE 1.27

1.2.7.1 GRAPHIC DESIGNER

Graphic designers plan the final printed/published product, guiding the style and mood of the piece. Designers should have a natural artistic talent as well as an eye for detail and color. The designers use their artistic talent with various imaging software and traditional design tools to arrange the words and visuals for their designs. Graphic design job offerings and availabilities change with time, technology and need. But the common description is that of a visual communicator, regardless of medium.

FIGURE 1.28

Graphic design has been steadily gaining ground as a qualified profession. Since 1914, the American Institute of Graphic Arts (now AIGA) has been growing in parallel to the disciplines of design. In 1954, the AIGA had 1,324 members, and in 2008, its membership was 22,309.

Often labeled as "communication design," graphic design frequently happens in partnership with marketing, publishing and similar information-oriented fields. While illustrators prioritize artistry, graphic designers are focused on conveying a message (artistically) to their audience.

Artists are often looking for ways to be creative and gainfully employed. Graphic design is one way to achieve both. Whether as freelancers or in-house talent, graphic designers are capable of adding creativity to a wide variety of products from business cards to billboards.

Those interested in graphic design should become members of the AIGA. This professional society not only educates future designers, but it also offers professional resources to attain and retain design employment.

The graphic design field has expanded in recent years with the growth of the web and electronic media. Traditional graphic designers worked in print media, environmental graphics, and broadcast and motion picture graphics. Today many designers work exclusively as graphic web designers, using specialized software to create graphics for the Internet. Salaries for graphic web designers vary according to factors such as location and type of company. Graphic designers specializing in web site design and animation have the best job prospects in today's competitive job market, according to the Bureau of Labor Statistics. In 2008, graphic designers held just over 286,000 jobs in the United States. According to the Bureau of Labor Statistics, employment prospects for graphic design professionals is expected to grow by 13 percent through 2014. The demand for graphic design professionals is expected to increase as the demand for interactive design and media increases.

Web designer salaries are higher in some areas than others. The cost of living varies by geographic area also. Web designers in Atlanta, Georgia, were right at the national average of $55,000 in 2010, according to the Aquent survey. Chicago web designers earned $57,000 in 2010. Los Angeles web designers earned an average of $60,000 for 2010. Web designers in New York City earned an average of $70,000 in 2010, according to the Aquent survey. Average salaries for graphic web designers vary according to the type of company. Web designers working for graphic design firms earned an average salary of $55,000 in 2010, according to the Arquent survey. Those working for advertising agencies earned an average income of $56,000, while those working in the publishing industry earned an average of $60,000 for 2010. The average salary for web designers at web development firms was considerably less at $45,000 for 2010, according to the Arquent Survey.

The Bureau of Labor Statistics published the mean annual wage of all graphic designers at $47,820 as of May 2009. The bureau cites higher average salary figures for the same period of $55,150 for computer design and related services, and an average salary of $62,810 for multimedia artists and animators. Each of these categories include, but are not limited to, graphic web designers.

1.2.7.2 ILLUSTRATOR

Illustrators develop the visuals---artwork, graphs, charts---that pair with words. An illustrator must have precise artistic talent as well as knowledge of composition and proper use of the tools of the craft. Illustrators use hand-drawn art and computer-created images to create their visuals.

Graphic illustration is the centerpiece of all forms of print and digital communication. Whether it's a brochure, web site, blog or poster; there is a dedicated graphic illustrator conceptualizing and designing the illustration for each medium. Being a graphic illustrator not only requires an artistic eye, but she must also be able to meet critical deadlines and deal with a wide range of personality types to get each job done effectively for the client.

Graphic illustrators must have a solid background in art and design. This type of education is often best facilitated at an art school where students can specialize in different areas of graphic design. Graphic illustration also requires extensive training in industry-standard design and multimedia software. A degree in graphic design or illustration is not always necessary, but graphic illustration is a skill that can be best perfected in the two to four years a degree may require.

An illustrator's most valuable skill is the ability to conceptualize and create compelling graphic illustrations for their clientele or employers. Additionally, this also includes the ability to adapt to frequent changes within a certain project. A client or boss may want to completely change a design in favor of a new artistic direction. A good graphic illustrator must also be able to navigate the complicated nature of interpersonal relations that come with working with people.

Graphics illustrators more often than not, work as independent contractors and operate their own business. This also means graphic artists work with companies in a lot of different industries, and a company's expectations may vary greatly from industry to industry. For instance, designing a poster for a rock band might not have stringent requirements attached to the project. You may be able to complete the project without ever meeting the band in person. Whereas designing a brochure for a large computer software company may require that you meet several times a week.

The average graphic illustrator earns anywhere from $30,000 to $60,000 annually as of 2010. This varies from industry to industry and from city to city.

1.2.7.3 ELECTRONIC PREPRESS TECHNICIAN

Electronic prepress technicians operate advanced computers to manage prepress procedures like plate making, camera operation and film assembly. The functions performed in electronic prepress are preflighting, scanning of images, file repair, trapping, imposition, and outputting of film, proofs and plates.

1.2.7.4 PRESS OPERATOR

Press operators run the printing presses that create the final, physical product. Press operators must know the mechanical workings of the machine, possess good manual dexterity, and think quickly on their feet in order to produce a good quality product. Because of continued technological advances, operators need continued education with the related computerized pressing machines.

1.2.7.5 PRODUCTION MANAGER

Production managers oversee the overall production process for printed materials. When a printing company receives a project, the production manager keeps the project moving and ensures it meets the client's needs by coordinating the project from layout to color matching to printing to distribution. Production managers should be well-organized individuals, able to plan ahead, foresee and troubleshoot problems, and be level-headed in their dealings.

In the graphic communications field, it is the art director's responsibility to formulate a design concept and supervise the copywriters, photographers and artists who execute the concept. The U.S. Department of Labor's Bureau of Labor Statistics notes that art directors usually are promoted after gaining several years of experience in an advertising or design firm. A bachelor's degree is a general requirement for art directors.

Art directors earned a mean annual wage of $94,100 as of May 2010, according to the BLS' Occupational Employment Statistics survey. Salaries ranged from $42,840 for the bottom 10 percent to $163,430 for the top 10 percent. The median annual wage for this occupation was $80,630. The bureau calculated mean annual wages by multiplying the mean hourly wage of $45.24 by 2,080 -- the average number of hours worked by a full-time employee.

Advertising services was the largest employer for art directors, paying them a mean annual wage of $95,860. Specialized design services and newspaper publishers were other industries that employed large numbers of art directors, with mean annual wages of $99,770 and $81,340, respectively. Legal services was the highest-paying industry for art directors, with a mean annual wage of $185,830. As of May 2010, there were 29,700 art directors employed in the U.S., according to the BLS.

The five states that reported the highest employment levels for art directors were California, New York, Illinois, Texas and Ohio. Salaries in these states ranged from $77,590 in Texas to $128,080 in New York, which also ranks as the highest-paying state for art directors. The highest-paying metropolitan area for art directors was Poughkeepsie, New York, where the mean annual wage was $152,480. Four of the 10 highest-paying metropolitan areas for art directors were in the state of New York, according to data released by the BLS.

The BLS reports that employment for art directors will grow by 12 percent through the year 2018. Job growth will primarily be in the advertising industry, while publishing opportunities will decline, the bureau notes. However, competition will be "keen" because there are more qualified candidates than available jobs. Earning a graduate degree in a field such as arts management can increase job prospects for an art director.

1.2.7.6 PAGE-LAYOUT ARTIST

Page-layout artists outline a piece's text and artwork to match the graphic designer's plan. The page-layout artist combines the works of many---illustrator, designer, copywriter---to create the final product. The job requires precision, accuracy, neatness and the ability to follow directions.

1.2.8 CAREER CHOICES IN COMPUTER AIDED DESIGN (CAD)

CAD, or Computer Aided Design, is a generic description for a wide range of software applications. CAD designer jobs cover a huge scope of industries, some quite different, like architecture and fashion. Computer Assisted Design software is used to do detailed plans and designs of products to industrial standards.

CAD is now the primary design methodology in all industries. It's a uniquely adaptable method for producing detailed plans of products, and is an essential qualification for all engineers and industrial designers. It includes 2D and 3D modeling, and is capable of creating highly detailed, fully measured designs according to specifications. Learning computer-aided drafting programs such as AutoCAD are critical in this profession because much of the estimating and drawings are done via computer.

CAD training and qualifications may be obtained in various contexts in terms of career education. CAD elements are often part of formal education in some professions. In architecture CAD skills and competencies to fixed degree standards are required as part of formal qualifications. CAD training is also offered as a separate course for those wishing to enter the professions, or as a general introduction to the processes of CAD for students.

The cross-mix of qualifications required in CAD designer jobs can be considerable. Individuals interested in CAD drafting and computer design may find themselves in such career areas as architectural drafting, drafting design or general drafting. In architecture and civil engineering, CAD is often also required to conform to statutory requirements, and provide detailed plans suitable for use by manufacturers, builders, aerospace designs and onsite engineers. CAD training is therefore based on the requirements of the industry, and training is tailored to the specific disciplines.

CAD work ranges from the extremely detailed design of components to designs for whole aircraft and ships, buildings, urban planning and industrial machines. The workplace is highly structured, and plans and designs, like their products, are assembled in stages by the designers. CAD designers progress in degrees of difficulty from entry level basic designs up through advanced design schematics. This is demanding work, and the fact of being computer based only simplifies the modeling, not the complexity and detail of plans. CAD designers may have to spend days in constructing models to match specifications, working with varying levels of detail on components. CAD designs may have to be created to provide multiple levels of a design's structure, literally from the base through to full assembly of a product. Using CAD, it's possible to literally map an assembly from its most detailed components to its finished form. That's about as simple as it sounds. The CAD designer's work is under intense scrutiny at all stages for accuracy and meeting specification requirements. Designs made under commercial contracts must comply with contract requirements, within contract times. CAD designers can work long hours in this environment.

FIGURE 1.29 AutoCAD MOBILE APPLICATION (iOS)

Individuals who work in industries that use CAD drafting and computer design typically find themselves in positions such as drafters, estimators, CAD operators or project managers. These professionals utilize computer-aided design programs to prepare drawings, plans and sketches. These blueprints are then used to build a variety of things from buildings and machinery to toys and other manufactured products.

As any kind of drafter, you need to have the right mechanical skills and visual aptitude. Even though most of your work is done on a computer, you also need to be able to make accurate calculations and draw well. It is important to have good communication skills because you will be relaying information to engineers, architects and other professionals in the field who will utilize the information you produce. Your duties will be specific to the type of drafting you do, but in general, you will be charged with providing the visual guidelines and blueprints for any given project. You will need to provide measurements, dimensions and notes on materials needed to complete the project. A background and understanding of engineering and manufacturing may also be required. Good math and calculation skills are a plus.

There are a variety of training opportunities and programs available for those interested in CAD drafting, architectural drafting or computer design. Depending on the type of position you wish to acquire, you can enroll in a two-year program at a technical college, a four-year program at a university or obtain an advanced degree from an accredited school. Technical colleges will provide you with the technical skills needed in the field, whereas four-year colleges typical concentrate on a subject area (such as math, architecture or engineering). Wherever you choose to complete training, you'll want to make sure that you have developed your mechanical drawing and drafting skills and have general knowledge of drafting standards and engineering technology. Any program in the field should also offer extensive computer-aided design program training as well. Certification can be achieved on top of a postsecondary degree through the American Design Drafting Association (ADDA).

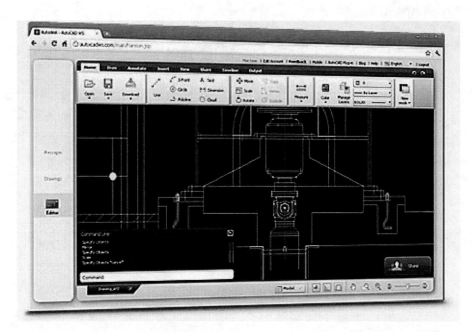

FIGURE 1.30 OPEN AND EDITDWG FILES WITH JUST A WEB BROWSER –AutoCAD WS

There are several career opportunities for those interested in using CAD drafting and computer design. Specific positions may include: architectural drafter, civil drafter, engineering drafter, electrical drafter, or mechanical drafter. Drafters at the entry-level typically work under supervision and may be given additional work after gaining adequate experience. There are many employers in this field who support and even pay for continued training and education. Drafters who take advantage of this and have appropriate accreditations can move on to become engineers, architects or engineering technicians.

In conclusion, CAD drafting and computer design can lend themselves to a variety of career options. Whether you wish to be a drafter, engineer or architect, it is important to have the proper training and education. You will need to acquire the technical skills necessary to perform in each specialty area. Employers will hire those with post-secondary education and training along with adequate technical skills.

The CAD designer's career pays back all the hard work in career opportunities. Advanced CAD designers are in high demand. They're indispensable to product design, and invaluable in quality control on design projects. CAD design businesses literally can't work without them. Experienced CAD designers have their own design portfolios, testimonies to their competence and experience. CAD experts can earn an excellent income as consultants, troubleshooters, and business advisers. Their expertise is a passport to the top bracket of their industries.

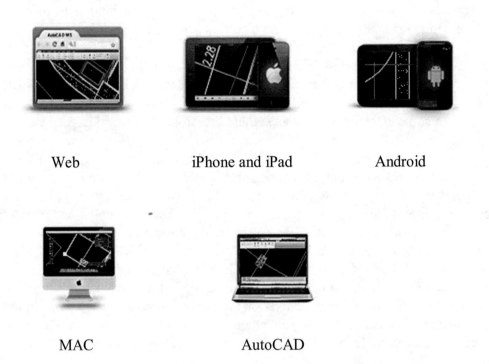

| Web | iPhone and iPad | Android |

| MAC | AutoCAD |

FIGURE 1.31 AutoCAD APPLICATIONS ON THE MOVE

1.2.9 CAREER CHOICES IN ELECTRICITY

The Technology – Electricity touches virtually every facet of our lives. Although it is a single discipline, A career in electricity, such as Electrical Engineering is best described as several related and intertwined technical areas: Automatic Control, Communications, Power and Machinery, Computers, and Electronics.

Automatic control systems include antilock brakes and cruise control, airliner autopilots, cruise missile targeting systems, automated manufacturing systems, building elevators, robotic manipulators, and the guidance system that enabled Project Apollo to land man on the moon.

Communications systems include cell phone networks, AM, FM, and satellite radio (e.g., Sirius and XM), high definition television (HDTV), and computer networks sustaining the Internet and the World Wide Web. One of the most active areas of communication research is the software defined radio. A software defined radio changes its function (e.g., AM, FM, satellite, etc.) based on the software executing in the computer around which it is designed - computers intertwined with communications and electronics.

Electric motors are key elements in hybrid automobiles and they drive the wheels of 4,400 hp Diesel-electric locomotives. Motors manufactured using rapidly advancing nano-technology are so small that hundreds would fit onto the end of a human hair. Electric generators can be viewed as motors "running backward." Generators convert mechanical energy from dams, wind, or coal fired steam turbines into electrical energy. These, along with a small contribution from solar energy, power the nationwide grid that reliably delivers electricity to our homes.

Computers are ubiquitous. They range from family PCs and Macs to powerful mainframes and super computer clusters used by the financial industry and scientific research community. Most computers are invisible! Microprocessors reside in televisions sets, iPods, cell phones, microwave ovens, and even some electric toothbrushes; there are probably several in your car.

Analog and digital electronic components are the building blocks used to construct many of these systems. They are designed by electrical engineers and often implemented on Integrated Circuit (IC) chips (a.k.a. microchips). Designers use Verilog and other hardware descriptor languages (HDLs) to design complex digital electronic systems including Blackberrys, iPods, and custom controllers for the automobile industry. Microcontrollers (tiny computers) are essential for building many medical instruments including imaging systems (X-ray, MRI, and CAT scans), heart pacemakers, and ultrasound devices. Your home entertainment center, many appliances and battery operated tools rely on electrical engineering designed electronics to function properly. Communications, Computers, Power Generation and Transmission, Analog and Digital Electronics, and Automatic Control are the fundamental areas that make up electrical engineering, areas that spawn exciting technological advances and exciting careers.

1.2.9.1 ELECTRICAL ENGINEER

Electrical engineers create, troubleshoot and oversee the building of electrical equipment. This includes all systems of an electronic device, from power generation, lighting and control equipment to any wiring the system may require. Electrical engineers design equipment for automobiles and aircraft with a general industry focus toward power generation and the ability of a system to supply enough power to run a device.

Electrical engineers are instrumental in revolutionizing the lives of modern man. They are required by the industries manufacturing all the household and office appliances like refrigerators, televisions, computer, microwaves and what not. In our age of satellite-transmitted television and transcontinental computer networks, these engineers are high in demand. Electrical engineers also find employment in atomic power plants, hydroelectric power plants as well as thermal power plants. Job responsibilities include specification, design, development, and implementation of products or systems, as well as research to create new ideas. This role provides a number of challenges ranging from problem identification and the selection of appropriate technical solutions, materials, test equipment, and procedures, to the manufacture and production of safe, economical, high-performance products and services.

Electrical engineering is the application of the laws of physics governing electricity, magnetism, and light to develop products and services for the benefit of humankind. Electrical engineering is a wide career field offering graduates many opportunities to find a niche for employment. Electrical engineers often find jobs working on power sources for electronic devices such as automobile ignition systems and airplane instruments, while others design electronic equipment and branch off into areas like computer hardware.

Electrical Engineering is a professional discipline that deals with the application of electricity, electronics and electromagnetism. This branch offers exciting job opportunities for students in the rapidly evolving fields of information and communication technology and the latest advances in the more traditional areas of power, control, and electromagnetism. So electrical engineering deals with the problems associated with large-scale electrical systems such as power transmission and motor control.

Research and specialization can be carried out in any of the following fields:

- Circuit Analysis
- Electro-Magnetism
- Solid-State Electronics
- Electric Machines
- Electric Power Systems
- Digital Logic Circuits
- Computer Systems
- Communication Systems
- Electro-Optics
- Instrumentation
- Control Systems

1.2.9.2 ELECTRONICS ENGINEER

Electronics engineers have a subtle yet important divergence from electrical engineers. Where electrical engineers focus mainly on generating and supplying power needed to operate systems, electronics engineers work on applications of electricity to maintain signal processing or the control of systems. Electronics engineers have worked to develop such systems as the modern GPS (global positioning systems), portable music players and equipment for broadcast television.

1.2.9.3 COMPUTER HARDWARE ENGINEERS

Computer hardware engineers are similar to electronics engineers, but they work specifically on computer hardware systems. These technicians work to develop central processing units, microprocessors and custom circuits that integrate into more complex computing systems, as well as disk drivers and printers. Computer hardware engineers also plan out the power requirements for personal computers and other computing devices by mapping out system performance through design specifications.

1.2.9.4 ELECTRICAL ENGINEERING TECHNOLOGY

Have you ever wondered how a DVD player works? Have you ever thought about the insides of a microwave while you were waiting for your popcorn to pop? You can indulge your curiosity by studying electrical engineering technology. You'll learn the engineering basics you need to understand how electricity and electronics work. And you'll get to try your hand at designing gadgets and solving technical problems. Students of electrical engineering technology learn the design, drafting, and technical skills they need to assist engineers and put engineering ideas into action.

FIGURE 1.32

A Bachelor of Science program in electrical engineering technology provides students with a foundation in circuits, analog and digital electronics, physics, calculus, and the liberal arts. The third and fourth years should expand on the fundamental courses with more advanced course work in applied differential equations, advanced circuits and electronics, transform methods, control systems, analog and digital electronics, mechanical engineering technology, and additional liberal arts courses. Students choose free electives or mechanical/manufacturing and professional electives to round out the program. Professional electives include sequences in electric power systems, electronic communications, embedded systems, telecommunications, networking, and optics. Students of electrical engineering technology learn the design, drafting, and technical skills they need to assist engineers and put engineering ideas into action. Furthermore, Engineering Technology (EET) programs prepare students to work in the areas of product design and manufacture, systems integration, plant operations, field support and engineering sales. The BS in many Electrical Engineering Technology programs are accredited by the Technology Accreditation Commission of ABET.

1.2.9.5 ELECTRICAL TECHNOLOGY

If you plan to work in industrial, commercial or residential electricity, then an Electrical Technology program is for you. This program will meet the training needs of two areas of concentration: Industrial Electrician or Construction Electrician. You will learn electrical theory, industrial motor controls, programmable logic controllers, electrical panel building, pneumatic/hydraulic circuits, residential wiring, commercial wiring and electrical troubleshooting. Laboratory activities will give you the opportunity to work with installation projects, switching and control equipment, typically used in problem solving procedures, and the maintenance of electrical equipment. Upon graduating from the Electrical Technology program, you will be ready for an entry level position in the industrial or construction trade. Employment opportunities are primarily with manufacturing, residential/commercial contractors and other various related fields. Students may obtain an Associate in Applied Science degree or a diploma in Construction Electrician, Industrial Electrician or Motor Controls.

1.2.9.6 ELECTRONICS TECHNOLOGY

Electronics Technology Program provides course work, competencies and experiences to prepare you for success in the areas of electronics, computer maintenance, mechanical, industrial, computer aided design, robotics and automation, communications, instrumentation and telephony.

Electronics Technology majors can work as electronic repair technicians, computer help desk technicians, communications technicians, chemical plant operators, network administrators, industrial maintenance, electronics technicians, instrumentation technicians, telephone LAN-WAN, network specialists, product support specialists, medical equipment specialists and much more.

Some of the average salaries for Electronics Technology graduates are: Chemical Plant and System Operators $49,199; Electronic Engineering Technicians $43,731; Telecommunications Equipment Installers and Repairers $43,065; and Computer Support Specialists $37,256. (Source: Kentucky Education Cabinet, Department for Workforce Investment, Office of Employment and Training, Research and Statistics Branch).

You have several options. Whether you are seeking a degree or just want a diploma, The following are credentials you can earn:

Associate in Applied Science Degrees

- Communications
- Computer Maintenance
- Electronics
- Instrumentation

Diploma

- Communications
- Computer Maintenance
- Electronics Instrumentation

Certificate

- Comptia A+
- Certified Cisco Network Associate (CCNA)
- Certified Electronic Technician (CET)

1.2.10 CAREER CHOICES IN CIVIL ENGINEERING & CIVIL ENGINEERING TECHNOLOGY

Civil engineers and technologists are involved in the provision of a physical facility from the initial study to determine whether it is needed and worthwhile, through conceptual planning and detail design, through the supervision of and actual construction, and then ensuring that it is operated correctly and maintained properly.

1.2.10.1 CAREER CHOICES IN CIVIL ENGINEERING

As one of the oldest engineering disciplines, the Civil Engineering program offers graduates a wide range of possibilities for work. Bridge and road construction are probably two of the first things that come to mind, but in truth these are only a part of the picture. Civil engineering involves the constant recreation, improvement and conservation of the environment, as well as the establishment of facilities such as buildings, roads, bridges, airports and dams that are required for the effective functioning of a community. Civil engineers aim to harness the forces of nature and the qualities of materials to provide physical facilities for the effective functioning of communities.

After their initial training civil engineering tend to specialize in one of the following:

- Geotechnical engineers design and construct foundations for structures and buildings, earth embankments, tunnels and earth dams.

- Transportation engineers plan, design and construct airports, railway lines and roads.

- Marine engineers design and construct quays, jetties, breakwaters and dry docks.

- Municipal engineers provide and maintain services (water, drainage and sewage facilities and networks as well as roads) in towns and cities. They also design and construct sewage, waste water treatment and purification plants.

- Construction engineers plan, control and execute construction projects. They are specialists in construction, the use of machinery, materials and human resources.

- Project managers are responsible for the management of a specific project.

- Structural engineers design and construct structures such as bridges, towers, frames or skeletons of skyscrapers, factories and power plant buildings. These engineers use concrete, steel and other building materials to construct stable, safe structures and buildings.

- Hydraulic engineers deal with flowing water, its storage, control and distribution. They are responsible for the planning, design and construction of dams, water supply systems and the sizing of bridge openings, drainage canals and flood control structures. The design and construction of harbors, deep-sea platforms, quays, jetties and dry docks are also the responsibility of the hydraulic engineer.

Civil engineers must visit the site and supervise proceedings. The working conditions depend on the civil engineer's field of specialization. Civil engineers should be proficient in Mathematics and Physical Science. They should be able to work well with other people and to communicate clearly. The ability to speak more than one language is an advantage. There is room in civil engineering for many different types of people: the scientific-minded designer and researcher; the public-minded planner of services which will affect the quality of life of entire communities; the outgoing leader of construction teams and the creator of complex organizations and systems.

There are several options open to the civil engineering professional, namely:

- With national, provincial and local government bodies. Here the emphasis is on the planning, construction, operation and maintenance of engineering facilities.

- Consultancies, where the emphasis is on planning, design and supervision of construction. A recent trend is to design and supervise the implementation of maintenance strategies.

- Construction companies, where the emphasis is the management of people and material resources to implement projects according to the design, specifications and contract conditions, agreed to with the client.

- Non-civil engineering companies employ professionals to ensure that the company is appropriately served in respect of their civil engineering needs.

- Some are employed in teaching and research facilities and institutions.

Qualified civil engineers with the necessary experience can work on contract basis for different companies. **Civil engineers** can practice on their own, or in partnership with other engineers.

FIGURE 1.33 CIVIL ENGINEERING AT WORK

Airports present a number of engineering problems. A fully loaded 747 weighs about 850,000 pounds, and slams down on the runway at very high speeds. In addition to the incredible force that this generates, civil engineers must take into account the number of wheels that a plane has, as well as their location and size to properly understand the stress that a runway experiences. The scale is equally impressive, as a typical runway is about 2 miles long, hundreds of feet wide and three feet thick. A good example of the size of civil engineering projects is the recently completed Denver International Airport. When it was finished, engineers had used 2.5-million cubic yards of concrete to build five 12,000 foot runways, aprons and taxi ways - this was placed atop six feet of compacted soil, a foot-deep soil spread, and eight inches of cement-treated base.

Bridges are some of the most beautiful and varied structures in the world. They have evolved over thousands of years from simple foot bridges to giant spans that cover thousands of feet. Construction techniques vary , from the classical cable-suspension bridge to the new stayed-cable design. The Akashi bridge is the longest suspension bridge in the world. At 12,828 feet long, it is an engineering marvel. Japanese civil engineers not only had to tackle the problem of spanning such a long distance, but also build a structure strong enough to withstand hurricanes, tsunamis, and upwards of 57 inches of rain per year. The Charles River Bridge in Boston is an example of stayed-cable design. Although not as grand in size as the Akashi bridge, it is no less of an achievement. Its designers had to route ten lanes of traffic through one of the busiest areas of Boston without interrupting the flow of existing roadways and T-lines. The structure is designed asymmetrically and supported by two inverted Y-shaped towers. These towers straddle the tracks of a railway at a 55-degree angle, providing more than enough room for passing trains.

Tunnels: Digging a tunnel big enough for even two lanes of traffic is a complex process. It is impossible to know the exact geologic characteristics of the excavation site prior to construction. As a result, engineers must create a plan that is flexible enough to work over a wide range of possibilities. Tunnels require enormous boring machines and other equipment, but are often needed in the most inaccessible of mountain passes. The supply of equipment is therefore an important issue, as are the environmental effects that the displacement of such a large amount of earth will cause. Imagine then the difficulty in constructing three tunnels under a total of 31 miles of land and ocean, between two different countries. This is exactly the task that Britain and France successfully completed in May 1994. As the culmination of a 200 year old dream, it was the biggest civil engineering project of the 20th century. In all, 13,000 engineers, technicians and workers were involved in the project, which made use of gigantic drills capable of boring through 15 feet of earth an hour. The amount of rubble removed increased the size of the United Kingdom by 90 acres.

Roads: A common career for a civil engineer is the construction and maintenance of the worlds roadways. These can range from the smallest city street to the enormous system of highways, on-ramps and off-ramps that allow us to get around each day. Engineers need to consider many issues when constructing roads, including vehicle safety, slope stability, and pavement durability. Transportation System Design: Another important field in the area of roadways is transportation system design. The flow of traffic is a complicated mathematical problem that anyone who's ever been stuck on a highway in rush hour can relate to. A transportation engineer is responsible for planning the layout of roads to maximize the flow of cars. They must work within the confines of extremely congested cities to create a solution that will keep people moving day after day.

Dams: A side effect of the great size of civil engineering projects is the huge number of jobs that they create. A perfect example is the Hoover Dam, built on the border of Arizona and Nevada during the height of the Great Depression. For five years, it employed more than 8,000 workers, engineers and technicians. To tame the Colorado river, these workers blasted giant tunnels through the sides of Black Canyon, which allowed them to work safely. At the time of its construction, it was the largest dam in the world. It is still the second-tallest in the United States. Civil engineers must always consider the environmental impact of their project. It is always nice to think bigger and better, but every achievement comes at a price. A good example can be found in modern-day China, where engineers are busy building the Three Gorges Dam, (site shown at right.) Widely regarded as one of the most beautiful areas in the world, the Three Gorges are home to a number of rare species, ancient temples and burial grounds, as well as millions of people. When the project is completed in 2009, it will be the largest hydroelectric dam in the world, spanning more than a mile across the Yangtze river, and generating 1/9th of the country's electric power. However, it will effectively eradicate the Three Gorges forever, and trap millions of tons of raw pollutants in the resulting reservoir.

Buildings: A successful building project achieves a number of goals. It must be structurally sound, not just today but fifty years down the road. It must achieve a complex integration of plumbing, electrical, and ventilation systems. It must interact positively with people on the inside and outside. Often, if must be built under tight financial budgets, and on a limited time frame. All of these challenges provide civil engineers with a number of exciting possibilities.

An interesting frontier in the area of skyscraper design is the ecotower. Using modern energy-saving technologies, these towers would consume much less power and generate fewer pollutants than the buildings of today. An example is a proposed 49-story building in London called Vauxhall Tower. If built, it will incorporate a 10-meter high wind turbine on top of the building generating electricity, a heating system drawing water from the London Aquifer for power, triple glazing to reduce heat loss. It would use two-thirds of the gas and electricity of a conventional building.

Water Treatment/Irrigation Systems: The problems involved in getting water to all of the people, farms and businesses that need it every day are numerous. Often, as in the southwestern United States, the supply of water is hundreds of miles away. Engineers must find ways to treat it and distribute it safely and quickly. In areas of extreme poverty, they must find a way to take existing water distribution systems, and make them safe using the technology and financial resources of the area.

Slope Stability, Mining, and Excavation: Slope stability is an important part of road and rail design, as well as large mining and building projects. Engineers must design slopes that will retain their size and shape under various loading and weather conditions.

1.2.10.2 CAREER CHOICES IN CIVIL ENGINEERING TECHNOLOGY

Civil engineering technologists help civil engineers to plan and build highways, buildings, bridges, dams, wastewater treatment systems, and other structures, and to do related research. Some estimate construction costs and specify materials to be used, and some may even prepare drawings or perform land-surveying duties. Others may set up and monitor instruments used to study traffic conditions.

Civil engineering technologists often work in support of civil engineering activities including designing bridges, highways or large complexes. They may assist in overseeing or monitoring construction, evaluating materials quality, reviewing surveying or mapping, or handling cost estimates and budgets.

Most Civil engineering programs are accredited by the Technology Accreditation Commission of the Accreditation Board for Engineering and Technology (TAC/ABET).

1.2.11 CAREER CHOICES IN CHEMICAL ENGINEERING & CHEMICAL ENGINEERING TECHNOLOGY

Everything around us is composed of chemicals. When chemicals react with each other newer forms of things are produced. Engineers and technologists applies the principles of chemistry, mathematics, physics, electrical and mechanical engineering. They are instrumental in the formation of so many new things around us. They continue to discover the existing materials for the use of mankind. Nowadays the applications of chemical processes are expanding in various industries so there is a greater need of chemical engineers now. Chemical engineers convert raw materials and chemicals into useful products and help in finding new materials and techniques of their usage. They design and maintain chemical processes of large manufacturing units. They are required as they work to create synthetic replacements for those natural materials and scarce resources.

FIGURE 1.34

1.2.11.1 CAREER CHOICES IN CHEMICAL ENGINEERING

Chemical engineers manufacture better plastics, paints, fuels, fibers, medicines, fertilizers, semiconductors, paper, and all other kinds of chemicals, by carrying out chemical reactions and purifications. They also play an important role in protecting the environment by inventing cleaner technologies. Some of these engineers are engaged in the work of finding ways to recycle the waste products. Some Chemical Engineers work in factories and some find jobs in laboratories. Some find employment in universities, consulting firms, engineering firms, mineral based industries, petrochemical plants, synthetic fiber industry, food processing units, explosive manufacturing industry, fertilizer industry, plastic industry, petroleum refining plants, pharmaceuticals, law offices, government agencies, and many other types of jobs. So we can see that these engineers have a varied amount of job options. Those who have an additional management degree are sought by private industries. In process industries they could work in positions such as a supervisor or manager, technical specialist, project manager or project engineers. They are also employed in a variety of manufacturing industries other than chemical manufacturing, such as those producing electronics, photographic equipment, clothing, pulp and paper and even in the development of aircrafts.

Chemical engineers work to transform raw materials or chemicals into new, useful materials. Large-scale manufacture work should be expected, as designing and constructing plants is a large part of most chemical engineers' jobs. Ensuring safe and economically-viable practices is essential, but there are opportunities in university research in addition to field work. As with electronic engineering, an undergraduate degree is essential, and many choose to study further. Chemical engineers earn around $61,000-$62,000 on average each year.

In the public sector they may be employed in defense establishment and atomic power plants, waste and water treatment department, environment regulation and recycling department, health related research projects, energy conservation projects. They are also employed in service industries such as scientific research and development services, particularly in energy and the developing fields of biotechnology and nanotechnology.

The academic program of chemical engineering lays stress on the subjects like Industrial Chemistry, Polymer Technology, Polymer Processing, Polymer Testing, Polymer Synthesis etc. The post graduate course work focus on areas like computer aided plant design, petroleum refining, fertilizer technology, processing of food and agricultural products, synthetic food, petrochemicals, synthetic fibers, coal and mineral based industries etc.

FIGURE 1.35 STUDENT EXAMINING BUBBLE RISE VELOCITIES

The specialized areas include research and studies in fluid mechanics, solid particle technologies, polymers, nonstructural materials, protein engineering, bio-catalysis, and biomedical devices. Another branch of specialization is Ceramic and Material engineering. Some of the other areas of specialization are Pollution control, Biotechnology, Pharmaceuticals, Metals, Fertilizers and pesticides, Automotive, Plastics, Manufacturing, Forensics, Thermodynamics, Food sciences, Cosmetics, Chemical safety, Education and training, Missile and space, Minerals and metals, Plastics and resins, Waste management.

Chemical engineers are employed across a wide range of businesses by both large and small companies. Chemical engineering remains one of the best-paying professions. Surveys show that chemical engineers earn more, on average, than other types of engineer and more than pure scientists.

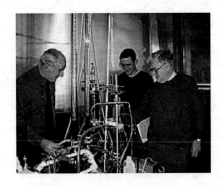

FIGURE 1.36

Even those graduates who choose not to accept jobs in industry are highly employable in other areas because they are experienced at solving problems and have good analytical and management skills. Chemical engineering graduates can go on to successful careers in finance, consultancy or scientific journalism, to name but a few.

The most popular career options in Chemical Engineering for technologists, engineers, and technicians are chemical industry and materials, food, consumer products, biotechnology and pharmaceuticals.

Chemical Industry and Materials

Chemical Engineers who work in the chemical industry typically perform research and development of the chemical reactions necessary to develop new materials and products. This career may also involve analyzing the properties of various materials and understanding the changes in atomic properties as a material changes its structure. A Chemical Engineer in this career may also study polymers and their chemical and statistical thermodynamic properties. Crystalline structures are also studied, as researchers try to create materials with specific, desired properties.

Food

Chemical Engineers who work in the food industry can work in agriculture or in manufacturing. Those working in agriculture may study the genetic modification of fruits and vegetables and attempt to increase yields and make them more desirable and thus more profitable. The career may also include researching methods of making agriculture more environmentally friendly, trying new methods of processing waste and conserving soil and water. Chemical Engineers, working in manufacturing, try to improve products or develop new products and optimize the manufacturing process to increase profits.

Consumer Products

All consumer products involve chemicals, and research to develop and improve a product requires a Chemical Engineer. Such a career may involve improving such consumer goods as hygiene products, chemical cleaning products and electronics.

Biotechnology

Chemical Engineers, working in biotechnology, typically work in conjunction with researchers in molecular biology, biochemistry, genetics, embryology and cell biology. A career in biotechnology may overlap with work in health care, crop production, agriculture and the environment. A researcher may use Chemical Engineering to advance procedures in genetic testing and gene therapy. Chemical Engineers in medicine may also work on engineering organisms and microorganisms to be used in applications, such as degrading wastes and converting chemicals into more useful ones.

Pharmaceuticals

Chemical Engineers working in the medical field can work on pharmaceuticals or perform research into new medical devices and procedures. A career in pharmaceuticals involves finding new medicines and medical solutions to diseases and other medical conditions. Pharmaceutical research can involve creating synthetic analogues of natural products, such as insulin. Chemical Engineers may also use bacteria, animal and plant cells to increase understanding of diseases, disease pathways and human responses to drugs.

1.2.11.2 CAREER CHOICES IN CHEMICAL ENGINEERING TECHNOLOGY

Careers in chemical technology are more rewarding today than ever. Technologists and technicians are in high demand for bringing valuable skills to the development of new products, processing methods, and materials. As critical members of scientific teams, they are at the heart of operations in the chemical industry, helping to get products and services to customers.

Chemical technologists and technicians work in every aspect of the chemical process industry, from basic research to hazardous waste management. Research and development technologists and technicians work in experimental laboratories, and process control technicians work in manufacturing or other industrial plants. They operate many kinds of equipment and instrumentation, set up apparatus for chemical reactions, prepare compounds, monitor commercial production, test for product quality, and collect and analyze samples produced through organic synthesis. They conduct a variety of laboratory procedures, from routine process control to complex research projects. They also work in data management, quality control, and shipping to provide technical support and expertise for these functions.

Chemical technologists and technicians are vital members of self-directed work teams. They sometimes work independently. Most are hired on a "nonexempt" basis. That is, they work a 40-

hour week and are paid overtime for additional work hours. The workday can be very long when it involves big projects. Technologists and technicians tend to be on the move during the day, with a variety of responsibilities. They often report to more than one person. They work indoors, and some work in the field taking samples and measurements.

1.2.11.3 PLASTICS TECHNOLOGY

A plastic is a type of synthetic or man-made polymer; similar in many ways to natural resins found in trees and other plants. Webster's Dictionary defines polymers as: any of various complex organic compounds produced by polymerization, capable of being molded, extruded, cast into various shapes and films, or drawn into filaments and then used as textile fibers. Plastics are being used since 100 years and they are relatively new if we compare them with other materials. Since the 1970s, we have witnessed the advent of 'high-tech' plastics used in fields such as health and technology. New types and forms of plastics with new or improved performance characteristics continue to be developed. Plastics are used in such a wide range of applications because they are uniquely capable of offering many different properties that offer consumer benefits unsurpassed by other materials. They are also unique in properties and can be used for packaging, to plastic plants, to domestic items, containers, pipes and automobile parts and what not.

Plastics engineering encompasses the processing, design, development, and manufacture of plastics products. Chemical engineering is the father of polymer engineering, which involves designing of processes and equipment for producing new and different types of synthetic material.

The plastics and polymer industry is growing at fast pace. The transport sector, household appliances and goods, packaging and electricity and telecommunication are the major areas, which demand plastics, hence are creating employment opportunities in this sector. For instance, synthetic rubber is now in great demand.

Many private companies that deal with the production and marketing of plastic commodities also offer employment to plastics technologists and engineers. Plastic technologists also play a significant role in the key sectors of the economy, including agriculture and water management, automobiles and transportation, building and construction, telecommunication and electronics, besides defense and aerospace, computers and power transmissions and even in manufacture of artificial limbs.

1.2.12 CAREER CHOICES IN MEDICAL TECHNOLOGY

A medical technologist career involves using highly complex medical equipment to run sophisticated tests in laboratories. There are various kinds of tests run in these labs, such as chemical, microscopic, bacteriological, and hematological. The tests are performed on bodily fluids and other specimens, which can include saliva, urine, blood, and stool samples. In addition to running the actual tests, which are used for diagnosing conditions ranging from HIV/AIDS to cancer, medical technologists must also verify the accuracy of the test results. They're often called upon by physicians and other medical specialists for their input on which tests should be run. The demand for these medical jobs is growing fast.

The work is extremely detail oriented and requires a high level of native intelligence, as well as specialized education in order to qualify for the position. There are two classifications of the people working in a medical technologist career: - those with higher levels of education are known as clinical laboratory scientists, while those medical technologists with lower levels of educational attainment are classified as medical laboratory technicians. It's imperative to keep these distinctions in mind when considering a medical technologist career; there is much confusion between the two terms, as there is considerable overlap between both tiers. Clinical laboratory scientists (CLSs) and medical laboratory technicians (MLTs) often perform the same tasks, but the CLS designation carries more authority and commands higher salaries than the MLT label. In addition, the CLS may choose to specialize in a particular area, such as immunology, genetics, microbiology, hematology, biochemistry, bacteriology, etc.

FIGURE 1.37

In order to qualify for a medical technologist career, a person must earn a specialized college degree. To become a clinical laboratory scientist, one must earn a bachelor's degree in medical technology or clinical laboratory science. Generally such a degree will involve three years of classroom instruction and a fourth year of working an unpaid internship in a medical laboratory. A third option to qualify as a CLS is to earn a bachelor's degree in one of the life sciences, and then take an accredited program focusing strictly on medical technology. To qualify for the MLT designation, an associate's degree in medical technology is required. This will cover much of the same course material as the bachelor's degree, but won't include many of the non-medical courses required for a bachelor's degree. After graduating, the prospective medical technologist must also pass a rigorous certification test. For a CLS career, the appropriate test is the Medical

Technologist (MT) exam. The Medical Laboratory Technician (MLT) exam is given for those aspiring to become MLTs.

Salaries for both classifications are excellent, but, as stated earlier, they are much higher for a person with a CLS title than the MLT title, because of the higher level of education involved, and the fact that so many CLSs choose to specialize. As of this writing, most CLSs earn between $45,000 and $65,000 a year, with quite a few earning significantly more than that. The bulk of MLTs earn between $30,000 and $45,000 a year, and many earn more than that. Of course, MLTs can always enhance their earning potential by going back to school and getting the higher degree, and many employers are happy to pay for the cost of tuition for those with the drive and ambition to do so. For both classifications, job prospects for the next several years are projected to hold steady. A medical technologist career is both prestigious and rewarding, and should be an excellent career choice for a long time to come.

1.2.13 CAREER CHOICES IN MECHANICAL ENGINEERING & MECHANICAL ENGINEERING TECHNOLOGY

Mechanics, energy and heat, mathematics, engineering sciences, design and manufacturing form the foundation of Mechanical Engineering and Mechanical Engineering Technology. Mechanics includes fluids, ranging from still water to hypersonic gases flowing around a space vehicle; it involves the motion of anything from a particle to a machine or complex structure.

FIGURE 1.38

1.2.13.1 CAREER CHOICES IN MECHANICAL ENGINEERING

Mechanical engineering is one of the largest, broadest, and oldest engineering disciplines. Mechanical engineers use the principles of energy, materials, and mechanics to design and manufacture machines and devices of all types. They create the processes and systems that drive technology and industry. The key characteristics of the profession are its breadth, flexibility, and individuality. The career paths of mechanical engineers are largely determined by individual choices, a decided advantage in a changing world.

Mechanical engineers research, design, develop, manufacture, and test tools, engines, machines, and other mechanical devices. Mechanical engineering is one of the broadest engineering disciplines. Engineers in this discipline work on power-producing machines such as electric generators, internal combustion engines, and steam and gas turbines. They also work on power-using machines such as refrigeration and air-conditioning equipment, machine tools, material-handling systems, elevators and escalators, industrial production equipment, and robots used in manufacturing. Some mechanical engineers design tools that other engineers need for their work. In addition, mechanical engineers work in manufacturing or agriculture production, maintenance, or technical sales; many become administrators or managers.

A mechanical engineer is a person who designs, invents and builds everything from toys to tools to medical devices. He or she uses the scientific principles of motion, energy and force to find solutions to mechanical problems. The generalist nature of this specialization gives it a depth of range greater than any other engineering field, allowing for occupational flexibility. This is an occupation that offers a high level of job security because in essence, everything that operates using mechanics or scientific forces has been created, and will continue to be created and maintained, by a mechanical engineer.

FIGURE 1.39

Studying as a mechanical engineer requires you to undergo four to six years of learning about different scientific principles that pertains to this course. As you graduate, you have to take a licensure exam to eligibly practice your career.

To widen your choices, you can pursue a higher education in post-graduate level such as master's and doctorate. There are also the options that you can take in studying unrelated degrees which can help you to have a bigger scope of practice.

There are many job opportunities, which will be opened to you by the time you pass the licensure exam. Because of the nature of this discipline, it could encompass a great deal of different career path. You can explore work areas such as Environmental fields, Robotics, Biotechnology, Biomedical Engineering, Medical Technology, Manufacturing diverse materials, Marine Technology, Mining and Transport Industries and Acoustics. All these have their advantages and disadvantages respectively. In general, your job description might involve designing, managing, researching or developing projects. Furthermore, you can explore other related fields of mechanical engineering such as sales, industrial archeology, technical writing and software engineering. The various field of work for mechanical engineering could widely be stretched to Engineer Consultant, Petro-chemical companies, material development, service provider, manufacturing, communication, construction services, aerospace, research and development, teaching facilities, and the military.

Demand for mechanical engineers will continue to grow exponentially with the demand for more efficient and advanced machinery, particularly in the manufacturing sector which is the largest employer of mechanical engineers. Nearly half of the approximately 250 000 mechanical engineers working in the United States are employed in this sector, in the areas of fabrication, transportation, design, building and maintenance of tools and plant.

Graduates with a Bachelor Degree in Mechanical Engineering can expect to earn a starting salary of around $50,000 per year, one of the best starting rates of all professions. Depending on experience and field of expertise this can increase to over $100,000 at the top of the pay scale. In 2006 the median wage for a mechanical engineer was $69,850 with the highest 10% earning $104,900 (US Bureau of Labor Statistics).

1.2.13.2 CAREER CHOICES IN MECHANICAL ENGINEERING TECHNOLOGY

The field of Mechanical Engineering Technology (MET) is concerned with the application of scientific and engineering knowledge in support of engineering activities. The Mechanical Engineering Technologist's mission is to provide the professional services needed to transform the results of scientific and engineering endeavors into useful products and services. MET's perform the necessary analysis and create plans to convert designs into finished products in the most efficient and safe manner. The MET is the professional who produces design drawings and sets up and operates manufacturing equipment, handles inspections, analyzes production problems, and manages the implementation of improvement activities and/or projects.

The Bachelor of Science in Mechanical Engineering Technology, which focuses on product and process design, addresses today's job market and emphasize courses that include product design, tool and machine design, and manufacturing methods, as well as supporting engineering professions such as development engineers, application engineers, CAD engineering specialties, and basic engineering problem solvers. The courses at the Bachelor's Degree level allow the student to link the design aspect of product development to the production phase and facilitate delivery to the customer. Students learn the theory and application of hydraulics, pneumatics, dynamics, instrumentation, thermodynamics and heat transfer, and machine design. Additionally, students gain knowledge in mechatronics, materials and inventory control, and plastics design. Most Bachelor of Science Degrees in Mechanical Engineering Technology are accredited by the Technology Accreditation Commission of ABET (TAC/ABET).

Figure 1.40

An exceptionally varied range of career choices and directions are possible for students who choose a career in mechanical engineering technology. Some of the career paths available include:

- machine and product design
- product and system evaluation
- research laboratory experimental support
- prototype testing and evaluation
- plant operation and management
- energy production (includes conventional power plants, plus emerging energy alternatives such as wind, solar, geothermal, hydro, and others)
- quality assurance
- technical sales
- manufacturing system design / enhancement

- quality control
- refrigeration and HVAC system design / support
- energy exploration

Many mechanical engineering technology graduates are employed in the power generation industry, the aviation industry, the oil industry, and at government research institutions.

1.2.14 CAREER CHOICES IN INDUSTRIAL ENGINEERING & INDUSTRIAL ENGINEERING TECHNOLOGY

Who manages the flow of people at theme parks or airports? Who decides what kind of training employees need before they work with new equipment? Who produces the layout for the new facility? Who determines where to add people or machinery for maximum impact? If you like to be at the center of the action, designing creative solutions that make business and industry work safer, faster, and leaner, making organizations more efficient, productive, and cost-effective then the career for you is Industrial Engineering or Industrial Engineering Technology.

**FIGURE 1.41 RIVER ADVENTURE AT
UNIVERSAL STUDIOS IN ORLANDO FLORIDA**

Career opportunities involve problem solving in the fields of:

- Quality Control

- Production/Materials Management

- Information Systems

- Process Improvement

- Logistics and Supply Chain Management

- Systems Simulation

- Salary and Compensation Plans

- Workplace Design

- Personnel Management

- Occupational Safety, Health and Ethics

- Project Management

- Economic Analysis/Cost Control

1.2.14.1 CAREER CHOICES IN INDUSTRIAL ENGINEERING

Industrial Engineers (IEs) design, develop, implement and improve integrated systems that include people, materials, information, equipment and energy. This means that IEs improve complex processes in a variety of situations and industries. The process may involve the assembly line in a factory, the scheduling of aircraft for an airline, the operating room of a hospital, the loan transactions of a bank, etc.

IE is the only engineering discipline considering human characteristics & performance. Human factors and ergonomics are IE areas of study and you must have heard about ergonomic designs as they relate to computer keyboards, automobile dashboards, head-up displays for fighter planes, etc. IEs are in greater need now in an environment that includes downsizing, globalization and emphasis on efficiency and cost cutting. The implication of this is that IEs are very visible to top management and have great opportunities to advance to managerial ranks. IE is not a "behind the desk" job. IEs interact with other engineers, production/operations professionals, laborers, top management, customers and suppliers.

1.2.14.2 CAREER CHOICES IN INDUSTRIAL ENGINEERING TECHNOLOGY

Industrial engineering technologists study the efficient use of personnel, materials, and machines in factories, stores, repair shops, and offices. They prepare layouts of machinery and equipment, plan the flow of work, make statistical studies, and analyze production costs. Industrial engineering technologist typically work in areas such as cost estimating, facilities planning, manufacturing process design, production control, or quality assurance. Industrial Engineering Technologists work in teams with others to solve problems dealing with a work location, the layout of a plant, the flow of materials in a facility, production planning and control, the safety of workers, and quality control. They work in a wide variety of industries and fields, including manufacturing, medical care, transportation, software development, and government.

FIGURE 1.42

Industrial Engineering Technology (IET) is about determining the most effective ways to use people, machines, materials, and information to make a product or to provide a service.

As companies adopt management philosophies of continuous productivity and quality improvement to survive in the increasingly competitive world market, the need for Industrial Engineering Technologists is growing.

Industrial Engineering Technologists figure out how to do things better. They engineer processes and systems that improve quality and productivity. They work to eliminate waste of time, money, materials, energy, and other commodities and therefore save companies money.

CHAPTER 2
Preparing for a Career in Technology

CHAPTER 2
PREPARING FOR A CAREER IN TECHNOLOGY

2.1 PROFESSIONALISM AND ETHICS

Ethical issues are not clear-cut; but are based on believing there is a difference between right and wrong, deciding to do what you think is right when under pressure and assuming that other people are trying to do their best. Ethics can be violated in any profession, ranging from political leaders, lawyers, law enforcement officers, medical doctors, etc. It is believed that cheating in school, at sports and in business makes it more likely that someone will progress to a level of violating ethics and will feel comfortable in repeating these violations. There are pressures in the workplace that can possibly cause an employee to violate ethics and become unprofessional, such as productivity, solving a bad problem during a crisis and just the fear of not being able to do your job.

There are many unfortunate circumstances that can lead to a violation of ethics in the workplace; some of them are:

- Decrease in Morale
- Breakdown in change of command
- Burn-out
- Grievances and lawsuits
- Loss of productivity
- Damage to image and repudiation

Typical behaviors and mentalities that can lead to a violation of ethics:

- Misuse of funds
- Abuses of authority
- Winning at all costs
- Using people as a means to an end
- Making oneself an exception
- Not recognizing an ethical trap

Negative characteristics and devastating consequences that can lead to a violation of ethics:

- Not efficient
- An organizational liability
- Not a team player
- Damage to Career
- Damage to Future
- Unfit role model

Training, modeling, reinforcements and a sense of reality are the resolution to maintaining ethics. Family, School, Church and the media can play a strong influential role in valuing ethics. When people acknowledge right from wrong, respect the human feeling of others, recognize the sanctity of human life and live by the Golden Rule then ethical violations will be very low to no existence.

The Six pillars of character that will positively influence professionalism and ethics:

- Trustworthiness

    a. Honesty
    b. Integrity
    c. Promise keeping
    d. Loyalty

- Respect

- Responsibility

    1. Accountability
    2. Pursuit of Excellence
    3. Self-restraint

- Justice and Fairness

- Caring

- Civil Virtue and Citizenship

The five P's of Ethical Power:

1. Purpose
2. Pride
3. Patience
4. Persistence
5. Perspective

The Principles of a Morally Good Person:

a. Just
b. Trustful

c. Trustworthy
d. Moral Courage
e. Moral Autonomy

Living by principles, acting consistently, striving to be fair, practicing, seeking advice, realizing that the job will not be easy and not taking yourself for granted are inner strength realistic goals that can help prevent an employee from violating ethics. Having organizational values, walking the walk—talking the talk, training, modeling, discussion and nipping it in the bud are outer strength realistic goals that can help prevent an employee from violating ethics.

2.1.1 WHAT IS ETHICAL BEHAVIOR?

Ethics involves the definition and achievement of what is good or bad, right or wrong, in relation to moral duty and obligation. It also includes the need to act in accordance with the principles of right and wrong governing the conduct of a particular group, such as doctors and lawyers. In the study of ethics, it is critical to understand that the motive is as important as the act. If a person refrains from stealing only because she or he fears prison, she or he cannot really be viewed as ethical.

Ethics is concerned with encouraging you to do what you know you should do:

- Consider all relevant sides of an ethical problem.

- Consider basic ethical values.

- Act in accordance with the code of your profession.

Moral progress depends on our willingness to improve the consistency of our ethical judgment and behavior and to apply the same principles more thoroughly to our conduct involving other people. Primitive man recognized few, if any, obligations to those outside his tribe. But modern man in his shrinking world must recognize his obligations to humanity in general. It is much easier to hold ideals than to live up to them. To convince someone of his or her duty by reasoning, does not necessarily induce him or her to do it. Our decision of what to do in a given situation depends on our understanding of basic ethical principles and our common sense knowledge of the way of the world and its people.

EXAMPLE 1: An example of how ethics start with you.

If you obey the law, you will set a good example for others and spare your fellow Explorers or Advisors the discomfort of having to intervene in your private life.

One way to develop an ethical basis for decisions is to read, attend meetings, and cultivate an awareness of the kinds of situations that tempt people to behave unethically. An excellent starting point is to periodically review applicable codes of ethics, and apply them to recent situations in your experience. Discuss these situations with associates and friends in informal settings.

As you develop awareness, you will also develop foresight. You will learn to recognize situations early for their dangers. When you sense such a circumstance arising, stall for time or find a gracious way to defer a decision until you can think the matter over and consult with others. Always think ahead. Where could this situation go? Will it place me in a position where my ethical standards will be challenged?

Learn to see marginal or ambiguous situations more clearly.

Frequently ask yourself:

- "Is this ethical?"

- "Could it lead me to act unethically in the future?"

Ask certain questions during the early stages:

- "How would it look to someone else?"

- "Who else is affected by this decision and how?"

- "Is there an angle I'm not seeing?"

Cultivate one or more friendly but tough mentors – not yes-people. Your mentor need not be your boss, though you are fortunate if your boss would be tough-minded but helpful. You may need to try a few people out for their advice before finding those with the necessary depth of experience and understanding, and an interest in your development. A mentor who always gives you the easy answer – "No, there's no problem here" – is only teaching excessive regard for expediency. Find another one. They who walk with the wise shall be wise.

2.1.2 WHAT IS PROFESSIONALISM?

Professional behavior and ethics are interrelated. Ethics is the route through which professionalism becomes understandable, relevant, and practical. The topics of professionalism and ethics should be introduced early and reinforced throughout any professional program. Figure 2.1 shows an example of un-professionalism.

FIGURE 2.1

But it should be our job. Hopefully we can all agree. Isn't it important to work in a place where professionalism is exercised and understood by all your fellow co-workers and employees? Wouldn't we be serving our consumers and fulfilling the agenda appropriately? What is **professionalism** anyway? A lot of people don't know. Companies can go through training after training and discuss its importance and still professionalism is somehow lost. Some people just can't redeem themselves as professionals because they tend to forget one simple thing. Keep your personal business, personal. By doing this we are better able to prepare for a day that has criteria to be followed and completed. Whether or not that criteria needs to be met daily or yearly, like annual goals, it is important to play the part so that the short or long-term goal could be met. If we are not aware of our attitudes and behaviors at work, we could be responsible for not creating a healthy and professional work environment.

Four Tips on Professionalism:

- Loosen up at the same rate as your prospect or customer.

- Avoid bringing up personal matters in a new business relationship.

- Bashing competitors is taboo.

- Be punctual for all appointments.

FIGURE 2.2

Teamwork & Professional Demeanor is at the top of Figure 2.2. Teamwork at the workplace is very important because working as a team will allow all members to feel free to lend their ideas to collaborate and reinforce stronger ones. Teamwork will build strong work relationships and good work ethics.

FIGURE 2.3

2.1.3 THE CHALLENGE OF ETHICAL DECISION-MAKING

The term "moral behavior" is applied in evaluating the personal conduct of a citizen and is judged in comparison to society's norms. The term "ethical behavior" is applied to that citizen's conduct in professional matters and is judged in comparison to the standards of the profession, which are formally expressed in statements called codes of ethics.

Distinguishing between moral and ethical behavior is necessary because people have a wider array of value obligations when functioning as professionals than when resolving value dilemmas in their personal lives. A professional has specialized knowledge that must be applied to serve four entities: the employer, the client of the employer, the profession, and, most importantly, society. A professional also has legitimate moral obligations. In addition to the application of technical knowledge and the proper consideration of economic factors, the professional must properly balance the value obligations to each of the four entities. For example, the employee should be loyal to the employer, honest with the client, respectful of the profession, and sensitive to the health and safety of the public. Values such as loyalty, honesty, respect, and sensitivity to public safety are emphasized in professional codes of ethics.

For example in one scenario, rational ethical judgment by professional water managers is important because of the significant implications of their decisions to society. They make decisions that affect the environment, allocate water resources, influence public health and safety, distribute public monies, and affect the lives of future generations. Ethical conduct, or professional decision-making, is a necessary requisite to being called a professional. A professional must be able to properly balance competing values in making decisions that affect both society and the client, especially where personal, societal, and cultural values conflict. The value issues must be properly balanced within the framework of economic, political, and sociological constraints. Professional ethics must not be overlooked but valued as a critical factor in the successful management of water resources. Situations with ethical concerns require mature and rational value decisions. Mature ethical decision-making is not easy, and the professional often is criticized by those who feel adversely affected by the decisions.

In another scenario, the preservation of wetland systems is often in value conflict with economic development of the land. Worthwhile values are legitimately associated with both sides of the issue. The difficulty in quantifying the worth of public amenities provided by wet-lands often complicates decision-making. The water professional who supports wetland development may appear unethical. It is difficult to quantify the value of a wetland to fish and waterfowl in terms that can be compared to the economic value of transforming the wetland into a shopping mall that will be used daily by thousands of people. Would a code of ethics lead a water professional to preserve the wetland for reasons of public welfare, or to develop the land and thus serve the client and the public with fidelity?

FIGURE 2.4

"Codes of ethics" are the value guidelines that a professional must follow in order to remain registered as a member of the profession. Codes are not a list of do's and don'ts. Therefore, to a young professional, they may appear to be vague statements. For example, a code might state that the professional should hold paramount the safety, health, and welfare of the public, or that they should act as faithful agents in professional matters for each employer or client. The emphasis on values is evident through the terms "public safety" and "faithful."

When one is confronted by decisions related to water resources issues, such as sustainable development and wetland systems, interpretation of these guidelines is not always clear-cut. Differences of opinion can lead a professional to blow the whistle. Misinterpreting the codes or ignoring them can result in a person's losing his or her job, or even being expelled from the profession. Thus, understanding value issues and being able to make mature value decisions are just as important to the water resources practitioner as is technical knowledge.

2.1.4 PROFESSIONALISM AND ETHICS WHEN DEALING WITH CLIENTS

There is no substitute for professionalism and ethics when dealing with clients - common sense tells us that.

It is this professionalism and ethical conduct that gives certain contractors a competitive edge over others that fail to act like professionals.

When you have a written code of conduct that you present to your clients, and the client sees that you are in fact acting in accordance with that code, then there is a foundation for trust established. Satisfied customers become loyal customers that recommend your company to neighbors and friends.

Professional conduct for contractors:

- Treat customers with respect, being courteous and at all times law abiding.

- Enter into contracts for work they know they are qualified to perform, and stand behind their work, offering warranties.

- Are honest and straightforward with their clients, submitting reasonable proposals and answering all questions pertaining to those proposals.

- Communicate with clients, following up with any concerns or questions and responding quickly to any problems.

- Ensure daily clean-up of the job site and daily safety inspection before departing from the job site each day.

- Promote safety and recognize that everyone's health and safety are of paramount concern.

- Encourage proper dress and professional behavior, including refraining from the use of profanity on job sites and assuring a drug and alcohol free job site.

- Always strive to better service customers and promote professionalism and ethical behavior in every facet of their daily operations.

2.1.5 ETHICS AND PROFESSIONALISM IN THE WORKPLACE

Conducting yourself in the utmost professional manner is a great way to succeed in the workplace. Treat this time as opportunity to hone your professional skills by gaining valuable experience in the following:

ATTITUDE – Remember that you are representing your company, agency, institution, etc. At all times, do your best to present yourself in the best possible light. Many times, a positive attitude can make up for deficiencies in other areas, so be sure to put your best foot forward whenever possible. This is your chance to make a positive impression on the organization and to gain valuable skills necessary for success in the workplace. Make the most of every learning opportunity and be cordial and friendly with everyone you meet!

COMMUNICATION – Depending on the layout of the site, you may or may not have your own workspace. Remember to respect others' privacy by not asking about a coworker's age, relationship status, sexual orientation, politics, religion or health unless they offer the information first. Likewise, respect others by keeping your voice down when talking, as well as controlling your phone and/or computer volume. Be sure to turn off your cell phone or PDA when in the workplace.

DRESS – Be sure to follow the dress code of the office, if stated. If there isn't a set standard, observe what others wear and dress accordingly. A good rule of thumb is to dress as if you already have the job you want to get, which means you should always dress in a presentable manner. Likewise, practicing good hygiene is essential, and limiting makeup and fragrances is important. Finally, be aware of your jewelry, your hairstyle and visible tattoos as these are all important aspects of your professional image.

ETHICS - If you are faced with what you believe to be an ethical dilemma, be sure to address this with your site coordinator before making a decision. Likewise, be sure to talk about the issues with coworkers to get their advice. Be honest with yourself in what you are prepared to do. Remember, at no time should you be expected to engage in any illegal activity. Your actions and those of the organization should promote learning and a positive experience at all times. Again, don't be afraid to ask questions with your site coordinator or others within the organization.

NETWORKING - Your practice experience is meant to be primer for finding a position upon graduation. Learning about the organization is important, but so is learning from the professionals you will be working with. Take time to get to know them by learning what they do and make your presence known by asking pertinent questions, getting involved in projects and over-delivering on assignments. Be sure to follow up with contacts internally and externally even if they can't immediately help you. Remember, networking is a two-way street- being helpful to others can pay dividends for you in the long run.

PREPAREDNESS – Just as you would not want to be unprepared for a class, you do not want to underperform on your job site. Be mindful of deadlines and absolutely deliver on all promises. If asked to conduct research, work on a project or give a presentation, take on these assignments happily. Be sure to communicate progress and any difficulties with your site coordinator or the appropriate person. Remember that you are at the site to learn, so arrive ready to work without distraction. And don't be afraid to ask plenty of questions. Expect to learn about the organization and the industry and be able to speak intelligently when asked.

SEXUAL HARASSMENT & RELATIONSHIPS – Workplace relationships are generally subject to strict guidelines. Be sure to adhere to company policies should you enter into a relationship with a coworker. Should that or any work relationship cross certain boundaries, it may be considered sexual harassment. There are two types – quid pro quo and hostile work environment. Quid pro quo means "something for something", which refers to an employee performing sexual favors in return for a promotion or preferential treatment. Hostile work environment entails a coworker feeling uncomfortable about another's actions, including touching, flirting or inappropriate comments or materials. Sexual harassment is against the law and is taken very seriously. If you have questions regarding what is and isn't acceptable behavior, don't be shy in asking your site coordinator for direction.

TIMELINESS – Since you will be travelling to your site, plan to arrive early each day. Plan accordingly if you will be using public transportation, and be sure to factor in time to and from your parking site if you will be parking on site. You will be asked to set a schedule with your site coordinator, so be sure to discuss any tests or any conflicts early on. Never leave your assignment before the end of your schedule unless previously approved by your site coordinator. Communicate with your site coordinator as soon as possible if absent and be sure to discuss alternatives to make up any time missed.

2.1.6 MAINTAINING AND NURTURING YOUR REPUDIATION

Adhering to ethical standards is a very important attribute in having a solid professional career; however there are four key categories of attributes which deserve attention:

Personal and Professional Development

A professional should never stop learning. Formal and informal means of education are continually available. Strengthen your skills and keep up with changes and innovations, particularly in the area of technology. Read into other fields of study (we need to know each other's areas of learning). The act of communicating comes from the communications curriculum, what we are supposed to communicate comes from the other fields of knowledge. Helping you gain knowledge, obtain a membership in at least one professional association and actively pursue the educational opportunities offered.

Read the newspaper and professional journals, read the important new book that everyone's reading. Read magazines that broaden your knowledge of the world around you and keep yourself up to date on current events. As a professional, you will be interacting with people in personal, social and professional situations so you need to be able to converse about a wide range of current events topics such as technology, politics, sports and entertainment.

Learn from your colleagues, organize yourself and take part in the networking opportunities. Serve in organizations and do good work. Be a mentor to other up-and-coming professionals, and seek mentors you can ask questions and advice. Send appropriate notes of encouragement, thanks and congratulations. Send lots of holiday cards; this helps in keeping your network alive. Overconfidence often masks incompetence, always ask questions and be teachable and remain humble, and yet still remain confident. Admit to yourself that you always have more to learn.

Work Habits and Job Performance

Know your own strengths and weaknesses and own up to your mistakes. Otherwise, you'll never overcome your challenges. Prioritize tasks, allocate time, and work within constraints. Don't think about how long you have worked; focus on the success and results. Be goal-oriented, not just task-oriented. Pay attention to detail and always deliver work on time. Work hard and be absolutely dependable.

If you want to be promoted, do your job well and then help do the job of the person you would like to replace. Help that person whenever possible. When people are promoted, they often have a hand in selecting a replacement. Make yourself the obvious choice.

Personal Conduct

Always act in a professional manner and dress professionally. Always be on time. Be aware of what goes on around you. Observe procedures and power structures (formal and informal) and work with them. Always be ethical and never allow yourself to be persuaded to compromise your personal standards. The respect of others is directly proportional to your respect for yourself and your respect for them. Work towards a balance in your life. Don't live to work or you'll burn out. You will be too stressed to maintain other vital relationships in life. If all you have in life is your job, you might be good at what you do, but you'll be very dull. Cultivate other interests and relationships and be a generous contributor to charitable causes and serve in your community.

Human Relations

Be personable and likeable. Learn to work well with people, treating them as equals. Work with and respect administrative assistants and other staffers. They can help you succeed or cause you to fail. Know people's names (and proper spelling) and use them. Don't hold grudges and stay out of office politics for at least the first year in any organization. It will take that long to understand the formal and informal power and communications structure. Never ever believe the job could not be done without you, cooperation is the key to success. Show your gratitude to other team members openly and often. Give others credit freely for their contributions.

2.1.7 ETHICS AND PROFESSIONALISM FOR COMPUTER PROFESSIONALS

A. Ethics

1. Ethics and Responsible Decision-Making

The foundation of all security systems is formed by moral principles and practices of those people involved and the standards of the profession. That is, while people are part of the solution, they are also most the problem. Security problems with which an organization may have to deal include: responsible decision making, confidentiality, privacy, piracy, fraud & misuse, liability, copyright, trade secrets, and sabotage. It is easy to sensationalize these topics with real horror stories; it is more difficult to deal with the underlying ethical issues involved.

The student should be made aware of his individual responsibility in making ethical decisions associated with information security.

2. Confidentiality & Privacy

Computers can be used symbolically to intimidate, deceive or defraud victims. Attorneys, government agencies and businesses increasingly use mounds of computer generated data quite legally to confound their audiences. Criminals also find useful phony invoices, bills and checks generated by the computer. The computer lends an ideal cloak for carrying out criminal acts by imparting a clean quality to the crime.

The computer has made the invasion of our privacy a great deal easier and potentially more dangerous than before the advent of the computer. A wide range of data are collected and stored in computerized files related to individuals. These files hold banking information, credit information, organizational fund raising, opinion polls, shop at home services, driver license data, arrest records and medical records. The potential threats to privacy include the improper commercial use of computerized data, breaches of confidentiality by releasing confidential data to third parties, and the release of records to governmental agencies for investigative purposes.

The basic law that protects our privacy is the Fourth Amendment to the United States Constitution, which mandates that people have a right to be secure in homes and against unreasonable search and seizure. In addition, many laws have been enacted to protect the individual from having damaging information stored in computerized databases.

3. Piracy

Microcomputer software presents a particular problem since many individuals are involved in the use of this software. Section 117 of the copyright laws, specifically the 1980 amendment, deals with a law that addresses the problem of backup copies of software. This section states that users have the right to create backup copies of their software. That is, users may legally create a backup copy of software if it is to be held in archive. Many software companies provide a free backup copy to users that preclude the need for to users purchase software intended to defeat copy protection systems and subsequently create copies of their software. If the software purchased is actually leased, you may in fact not even be able to make backup copies of the software. The distinction between leasing and buying is contained within the software documentation. The copyright statement is also contained in the software documentation. The copyright laws regarding leased material state that the leaser may say what the leaseholder can and cannot do with the software. So it is entirely up to the owner of the software as to whether or not users may make backup copies of the software. At a time when federal laws relating to copyright protection are evolving, several states are considering legislation that would bar unauthorized duplication of software.

The software industry is prepared to do battle against software piracy. The courts are dealing with an increasing number of lawsuits concerning the protection of software. Large software publishers have established the Software Protection Fund to raise between $500,000 and $1 million to promote anti-piracy sentiment and to develop additional protection devices.

4. Fraud & Misuse

The computer can create a unique environment in which unauthorized activities can occur. Crimes in this category have many traditional names including theft, fraud, embezzlement, extortion, etc. Computer related fraud includes the introduction of fraudulent records into a computer system, theft of money by electronic means, theft of financial instruments, theft of services, and theft of valuable data.

5. Liability

Under the UCC, an express warranty is an affirmation or promise of product quality to the buyer and becomes a part of the basis of the bargain. Promises and affirmations made by the software developer to the user about the nature and quality of the program can also be classified as an express warranty. Programmers or retailers possess the right to define express warranties. Thus, they have to be realistic when they state any claims and predictions about the capabilities, quality and nature of their software or hardware. They should consider the legal aspects of their affirmative promises, their product demonstrations, and their product description. Every word they say may be as legally effective as though stated in writing. Thus, to protect against liability, all agreements should be in writing. A disclaimer of express warranties can free a supplier from being held responsible for any informal, hypothetical statements or predictions made during the negotiation stages.

Implied warranties are also defined by the UCC. These are warranties that are provided automatically in every sale. These warranties need not be in writing nor do they need to be verbally stated. They insure that good title will pass to the buyer, that the product is fit for the purpose sold, and that it is fit for the ordinary purposes for which similar goods are used (merchantability).

6. Types of Intellectual Property

Some people confuse patents, copyrights, and trademarks. Although there may be some similarities among these kinds of intellectual property protection, they are different and serve different purposes.

What Is a Copyright?

Copyright is a form of protection provided to the authors of "original works of authorship" including literary, dramatic, musical, artistic, and certain other intellectual works, both published and unpublished. The 1976 Copyright Act generally gives the owner of copyright the exclusive right to reproduce the copyrighted work, to prepare derivative works, to distribute copies or phono-records of the copyrighted work, to perform the copyrighted work publicly, or to display the copyrighted work publicly.

The copyright protects the form of expression rather than the subject matter of the writing. For example, a description of a machine could be copyrighted, but this would only prevent others from copying the description; it would not prevent others from writing a description of their own or from making and using the machine. Copyrights are registered by the Copyright Office of the Library of Congress.

What Is a Trademark or Servicemark?

A trademark is a word, name, symbol or device which is used in trade with goods to indicate the source of the goods and to distinguish them from the goods of others. A servicemark is the same as a trademark except that it identifies and distinguishes the source of a service rather than a product. The terms "trademark" and "mark" are commonly used to refer to both trademarks and servicemarks.

Trademark rights may be used to prevent others from using a confusingly similar mark, but not to prevent others from making the same goods or from selling the same goods or services under a clearly different mark. Trademarks which are used in interstate or foreign commerce may be registered with the Patent and Trademark Office. The registration procedure for trademarks and general information concerning trademarks is described in a separate pamphlet entitled "Basic Facts about Trademarks."

What Is a Patent?

A patent for an invention is the grant of a property right to the inventor, issued by the Patent and Trademark Office. The term of a new patent is 20 years from the date on which the application for the patent was filed in the United States or, in special cases, from the date an earlier related application was filed, subject to the payment of maintenance fees. US patent grants are effective only within the US, US territories, and US possessions.

The right conferred by the patent grant is, in the language of the statute and of the grant itself, "the right to exclude others from making, using, offering for sale, or selling" the invention in the United States or "importing" the invention into the United States. What is granted is not the right to make, use, offer for sale, sell or import, but the right to exclude others from making, using, offering for sale, selling or importing the invention.

7. Patents and Copyright Laws for Software

A patent can protect the unique and secret aspect of an idea. It is very difficult to obtain a patent compared to a copyright (please see discussion below). With computer software, complete disclosure is required; the patent holder must disclose the complete details of a program to allow a skilled programmer to build the program. Moreover, a United States software patent will be unenforceable in most other countries.

Copyright law provides a very significant legal tool for use in protecting computer software, both before a security breach and certainly after a security breach. This type of breach could deal with misappropriation of data, computer programs, documentation, or similar material. For this reason the information security specialist will want to be familiar with basic concepts of the copyright law.

The United States, United Kingdom, Australia, and many other countries have now amended or revised their copyright legislation to provide explicit copyright laws to protect computer program. Copyright law in the United States is governed by the Copyright Act of 1976 that preempted the field from the states. Formerly, the United States had a dual state and Federal system. In other countries, such as Canada, the courts have held that the un-revised Copyright Act is broad enough to protect computer programs. In many of these countries the reform of copyright law is actively underway.

8. Trade Secrets

A trade secret protects something of value and usefulness. This law protects the unique and secret aspects of ideas, known only to the discoverer or his confidants. Once disclosed the trade secret is lost as such and can only be protected under one of the following laws. The application of trade secret law is very important in the computer field, where even a slight head start in the development of software or hardware can provide a significant competitive advantage.

9. Sabotage

The computer can be the object of attack in computer crimes such as the unauthorized use of computer facilities, alternation or destruction of information, data file sabotage and vandalism against a computer system. Computers have been shot, stabbed, short-circuited and bombed.

B. Laws and Legislation

The types and numbers of security laws and legislation at all governmental levels are expanding rapidly. Often, we forget that such legislation may affect each of us, as well as the organization.

Some additional differences between a copyright and a trademark are as follows:

1. The purpose of a copyright is to protect works of authorship as fixed in a tangible form of expression. Thus, copyright covers: a) works of art (2 or 3 dimensional), b) photos, pictures, graphic designs, drawings and other forms of images; c) songs, music and sound recordings of all kinds; d) books, manuscripts, publications and other written works; and e) plays, movies, shows, and other performance arts.

2. The purpose of a trademark is to protect words, phrases and logos used in federally regulated commerce to identify the source of goods and/or services.

3. There may be occasions when both copyright and trademark protections are desired with respect to the same business endeavor. For example, a marketing campaign for a new product may introduce a new slogan for use with the product, which also appears in advertisements for the product. However, copyright and trademark protection will cover different things. The advertisement's text and graphics, as published in a particular vehicle, will be covered by copyright - but this will not protect the slogan as such. The slogan may be protected by trademark law, but this will not cover the rest of the advertisement. If you want

both forms of protection, you will have to perform both types of registration.

4. If you are interested in protecting a title, slogan, or other short word phrase, generally you want a trademark. Copyright law does not protect a bare phrase, slogan, or trade name.

5. Whether an image should be protected by trademark or copyright law depends on whether its use is intended to identify the source of goods or services. If an image is used temporarily in an ad campaign, it generally is not the type of thing intended to be protected as a logo.

6. The registration processes of copyright and trademark are entirely different. For copyright, the filing fee is small, the time to obtain registration is relatively short, and examination by the Copyright Office is limited to ensuring that the registration application is properly completed and suitable copies are attached. For trademark, the filing fee is more substantial, the time to obtain registration is much longer, and examination by the Trademark Office includes a substantive review of potentially conflicting marks which are found to be confusingly similar. While copyright registration is primarily an administrative process, trademark registration is very much an adversarial process.

7. Copyright law provides for compulsory licensing and royalty payments - there is no analogous concept in trademark law. Plus, the tests and definition of infringement are considerably different under copyright law and trademark law.

CLOTHING ITEMS

Here are a few guidelines about clothing items when it comes to copyright vs. trademark:

1. Anything you silk screen or otherwise display prominently on the front or back of a shirt, top, cap or hat is generally considered artwork, and therefore covered by copyright. In fact, if you send a photo of a clothing item to the U.S. Trademark Office showing your design, logo or slogan prominently displayed on the front or back, they will refuse to register it as a trademark.

2. To qualify as a trademark, your logo or slogan must be used as the brand of the clothing item itself. In other words, your logo or slogan must be used the way clothing brands are typically used and displayed on clothing, namely, sewn into a waistband, collar, hem or pocket, or applied to a label, sticker or tag, and NOT in a way that dominates the appearance of the clothing item.

3. The caveat, of course, is that when your design, logo or slogan is regarded as artwork - even though it can be protected by copyright - the protection only extends to the artistic configuration used. To put it more bluntly, if you have a slogan or name, copyright law can protect the artistic way you display it, but the text itself is NOT protected. Copyright law does not cover names, words or short phrases.

4. The only way to protect a name, word, short phrase or other text, is to register it as a trademark. But this means that you have to change the way you use the mark from an artistic

display to a brand name usage.

5. Yes, it is possible to register a design, logo, name or phrase under both copyright law and trademark law, so long as you use it in two different ways and you do it consistently. Keeping the two usages of the same design or text at the same time is not an easy task, and you can end up compromising your rights under copyright or trademark, or both, very easily if you aren't careful.

C. Professionalism

Students should be encouraged to become involved professionally while they are in school and to continue their professional involvement throughout their career. Several societies and professional organizations are concerned with security, including:

- The Computer Security Institute
- Computer Professionals for Social Responsibility
- Data Processing Management Association
- Security Management Magazine
- Licensing and Certification

2.1.8 ETHICS AND PROFESSIONALISM IN TEACHING

Teachers are not only masters of the content they teach, but they are also relay to their students' common societal values such as responsibility, respectfulness and conscientiousness. Teachers are always teaching, even when not delivering formal instruction, by virtue being a primary adult influence in a student's life. For this reason, professionalism and ethics are important topics in teacher preparation courses just as they are important considerations to parents of students and employers of teachers.

2.1.8.1 TEACHERS AS PROFESSIONALS-- STUDENTS

Professionalism in teaching refers to teacher interaction with students as well as teacher interaction with other teachers and supervisors. The former involves impartial teaching and appropriate teaching of all students, regardless of ethnicity, academic performance or personality. The professional teacher works hard to establish an equitable and safe classroom in which all students feel cared for and fairly treated.

2.1.8.2 TEACHERS AS PROFESSIONALS--COLLEAGUES AND SUPERVISORS

Professional teacher behavior with regard to colleagues refers to the way in which teachers interact with each other. A professional teacher is collaborative and individualistic; he or she will share materials when appropriate but does not become a burden to his or her colleagues. A professional teacher does not create personal alliances or feuds with his or her colleagues. With regard to supervisors and employers, the professional teacher is respectful and approachable; however, he or she maintains his or her sense of individual integrity. Clear communication with colleagues and supervisors is a mark of professionalism in a teacher.

2.1.8.3 ETHICS

Historically, ethics is the study of philosophical ideas of morality. The study of ethics is built around the question: What defines good and bad? Philosophers have considered this question to be of chief importance as a conceptual pursuit because it has application beyond the theoretical; good and bad and what defines something as such has a direct influence on society. Since educational practices do not take place outside of society and are directly related the culture in which they are based, ethics are an important part of any school or teacher.

2.1.8.4 ETHICS OF TEACHING

Because society still largely depends on the idea that there is good or bad, or acceptable and unacceptable, teachers must consider the ethical ramifications of their teaching styles and personal actions. This includes equitable treatment of all students as well as maintaining the proper student and teacher relationship. Ethics in education dictate that a high degree of responsibility comes with the privilege of teaching and mentoring a society's children, and teachers are to act accordingly.

2.1.8.5 PROFESSIONALISM AND ETHICS

The relationship between professionalism and ethics is significant. Professionalism in any discipline is defined by the responsibility to society of that discipline as determined by the society in which it is practiced. The responsibility of teachers is profound, and the professionalism expected great. Similarly, the ethics of teaching are derived from societal values and the importance placed on education. Teachers, as professionals who serve society, should abide with integrity by the expectations of professionalism and ethics set by that society.

2.1.8.6 PROFESSIONAL TIPS FOR SUCCESS

A professional learns every aspect of the job. An amateur skips the learning process whenever possible.

A professional carefully discovers what is needed and wanted. An amateur assumes what others need and want.

A professional looks, speaks and dresses like a professional. An amateur is sloppy in appearance and speech.

A professional keeps his or her work area clean and orderly. An amateur has a messy, confused or dirty work area.

A professional is focused and clear-headed. An amateur is confused and distracted.

A professional does not let mistakes slide by. An amateur ignores or hides mistakes.

A professional jumps into difficult assignments. An amateur tries to get out of difficult work.

A professional completes projects as soon as possible. An amateur is surrounded by unfinished work piled on unfinished work.

A professional remains level-headed and optimistic. An amateur gets upset and assumes the worst.

A professional handles money and accounts very carefully. An amateur is sloppy with money or accounts.

A professional faces up to other peoples. An amateur avoids others.

A professional uses higher emotional tones: Enthusiasm, cheerfulness, interest, and contentment. An amateur uses lower emotional tones: anger, hostility, resentment, fear, and victim.

A professional persists until the objective is achieved. An amateur gives up at the first opportunity.

A professional produces more than expected. An amateur produces just enough to get by.

A professional produces a high-quality product or service. An amateur produces medium-to-low quality product or service.

A professional earns higher pay than amateurs, and with that high pay come an higher expectation of professionalism and ethics.

A professional has a promising future. An amateur has an uncertain future.

The first step to making yourself a professional is to decide you are a professional.

2.2 TYPES OF FORMAL LETTERS WRITTEN TO EMPLOYERS

2.2.1 COVER LETTER

A cover letter is a letter of introduction to an employer, which is used to formally submit a resume for employer review. The purpose of the cover letter is to identify your intent to "apply for" or "seek out" a specific position within a company. It also formally presents you as available for a job position or range of positions within a company.

Most importantly, the cover letter is an opportunity to quickly introduce you and grab the employer's attention. Like the resume, it is another chance to market yourself to the hiring manager, promoting them to read your resume and ultimately grant a job interview.

A cover letter is a critical part of the job search process. It allows you the first opportunity to gain some interest from the employer. For most careers a cover letter must be submitted with every resume.

Cover letters generally fall into two categories:

1. Letter of application: applying for a specific, advertised opening.

2. Letter of inquiry: expressing interest in an organization, but you are not certain if there are current opening.

2.2.1.1 SELECT A COVER LETTER TYPE

When you need to write a cover letter, it's sometimes the small things that make a big difference. There are several types of cover letters that can be sent to employers and contacts. Be sure to choose a type of cover letter that reflects how you are applying for the job or the type of job search assistance you are requesting. Your cover letter should be designed specifically for the purpose you are writing and customized for each position you seek.

First of all, your cover letter needs to include your contact information (name, address, phone, email) so prospective employers can get in touch with you.

Your cover letter should include at least three paragraphs:

1. What you are applying for and where you found the job posting - First Paragraph
2. What you have to offer - Middle Paragraph(s)
3. How you will follow-up - Final Paragraph

In the first paragraph, if you are writing in response to a job posting, indicate where you learned of the position and the title of the position. More importantly, express your enthusiasm and the likely match between your credentials and the position's qualifications.

The second paragraph of your cover letter should refer specifically to the qualifications listed in the job posting and illustrate how your particular abilities and experiences relate to the position for which you are applying.

The final paragraph of your letter should reiterate your interest in the job and let the employer know how they can reach you and include your phone number and email address.

2.2.1.2 FORMAT YOUR COVER LETTER

How you format your cover letter, both from content (the information you include) and a presentation (what your cover letter looks like) perspective is important. Even when applying online or via email, your cover letter needs to be properly formatted, readable, and without any mistakes.

Cover Letter Format:

Your Contact Information
Name
Address
City, State, Zip Code
Phone Number
Email Address

Date

Employer Contact Information (if you have it)
Name
Title
Company
Address
City, State, Zip Code

Salutation
Dear Mr./Ms. Last Name, (leave out if you don't have a contact)

Body of Cover Letter

The body of your cover letter lets the employer know what position you are applying for, why the employer should select you for an interview, and how you will follow-up.

First Paragraph

The first paragraph of your letter should include information on why you are writing. Mention the position you are applying for and where you found the job listing. Include the name of a mutual contact, if you have one.

Middle Paragraph(s)

The next section of your cover letter should describe what you have to offer the employer. Mention specifically how your qualifications match the job you are applying for. Remember, you are interpreting your resume, not repeating it.

Final Paragraph

Conclude your cover letter by thanking the employer for considering you for the position. Include information on how you will follow-up.

Complimentary Close

Respectfully yours,

Signature

Handwritten Signature (for a mailed letter)

Typed Signature

2.2.1.3 REVIEW COVER LETTER EXAMPLES

Take the time to review cover letter examples; then make sure that your letter explains how your skills relate to the criteria listed in the job posting. When applying for a job a cover letter should be sent or posted with your resume. Your cover letter should be specific to the position you are applying for, relating your skills and experience to those noted in the job posting. Your cover letter is your first (and best) chance to make a good impression!

2.2.1.4 START FROM A COVER LETTER TEMPLATE

A cover letter template can be a good way to get started writing cover letters to send with resumes when you apply for jobs. Use a cover letter template as a starting point for creating your own personalized cover letter. Once you have a template ready to use on your computer, add your information to the cover letter template, then tweak and edit it to personalize your cover letter, so it highlights your qualifications for the job.

FIGURE 2.5

2.2.1.5 WRITE A CUSTOM COVER LETTER

It is important to customize your cover letter, so it presents your candidacy for employment effectively. It may be time consuming to write a custom cover letter for each job you apply for, but it's important to take the time and effort to show the company why you are a good match. Don't be afraid to try switching the format i.e. bulleted accomplishments versus. a paragraph, because the template is just a starting point for creating your own cover letter. Write a new customized cover letter for each job you apply for.

Save the original version of your cover letter, before you start making changes, so you can go back and start over, if you need to. Also, that way you'll be able to edit your original cover letter when applying for new jobs.

2.2.1.6 WRITE A PERSONALIZED COVER LETTER

When it comes to cover letters, taking the time to get personal is really important. Find out as much as you can about the company and the hiring manager. Personalize your cover letter and, if you can, address it to the individual responsible for hiring. If need be, research online or make a phone call to find out whom the hiring manager is.

If you know someone at the company, mention their name in your cover letter. Name dropping works - your cover letter will get a closer look if it mentions someone who works at the company. That's important both from your perspective and from the employee's, especially if the company has an Employee Referral Program and is eligible for a bonus. As an aside, be sure to ask your contact if they can recommend you for the job and help get your cover letter and resume a closer look from the hiring manager.

Mention how you learned about the job in the first paragraph of your cover letter. The company wants to know how the job was sourced, especially when you found the listing on a job board or other site where they paid to post. That sentence can simply say, for example, "I learned of this position from the posting I read on Monster."

Take it one step further and mention something about the company, from the mission statement on the company web site, for example, in your cover letter.

2.2.1.7 SEND AN EMAIL COVER LETTER

The most important part of sending an email cover letter is to follow the employer's instructions. If the job posting says to include your cover letter and resume as an attachment, attach Microsoft Word or Adobe PDF files to your email message. Save the files with your name, so they don't get mixed up with other applicant's materials i.e. alisondoyleresume.doc, alisondoylecover.doc.

When the employers requests a cover letter and resume in the body of an email message, paste your cover letter and resume into your email message. Use a basic font and remove the formatting. Don't use HTML. You don't know what email client the employer is using, so, simple is best because the employer may not see a formatted message the same way you do.

Be sure to include a Subject Line in your email with the position for which you are applying and your name. For example: Alison Doyle, Social Media Manager Position.

Include a signature with all your contact information - name, address, phone, and email address, so it's easy for the hiring manager to get in touch with you.

Send the email message to yourself first to test that the formatting works. If everything looks good, resend to the employer.

Figure 2.6

2.2.1.8 ADDRESS YOUR COVER LETTER

How to address a cover letter can be tricky if you are responding to a blind ad and don't have a contact person's name to include or you don't know the hiring manager's gender. Review Figure 2.7 to see how to address this type of cover letter.

Dear Mr. Jones

Dear Jane Doe

Dear Hiring Manager

To whom it may concern

Dear Human Resources Manager

Dear Sir or Madam

Dear Hiring Manager

FIGURE 2.7

There a variety of cover letter salutations you can use to address your letter. Employers who responded to a recent employer survey conducted by Saddleback College preferred:

- Dear Hiring Manager (38%)
- To whom it may concern (26%)
- Dear Sir/Madam (18%)
- Dear Human Resources Director (9.5%)
- Leave it blank (8%)

Once you have chosen a salutation, follow it with a colon or comma, a space, and then start the first paragraph of your letter. For example:

Dear Hiring Manager:

2.2.1.9 SEND YOUR COVER LETTER AS AN ATTACHMENT

When you apply for jobs via email, you may need to send your resume and cover letter as an attachment. It's important to send your cover letter and resume attachments correctly, to include all the information you need so your email message is read, and to let the receiver know how they can contact you to schedule an interview. Figure 2.8 shows how to send a cover letter as an attachment.

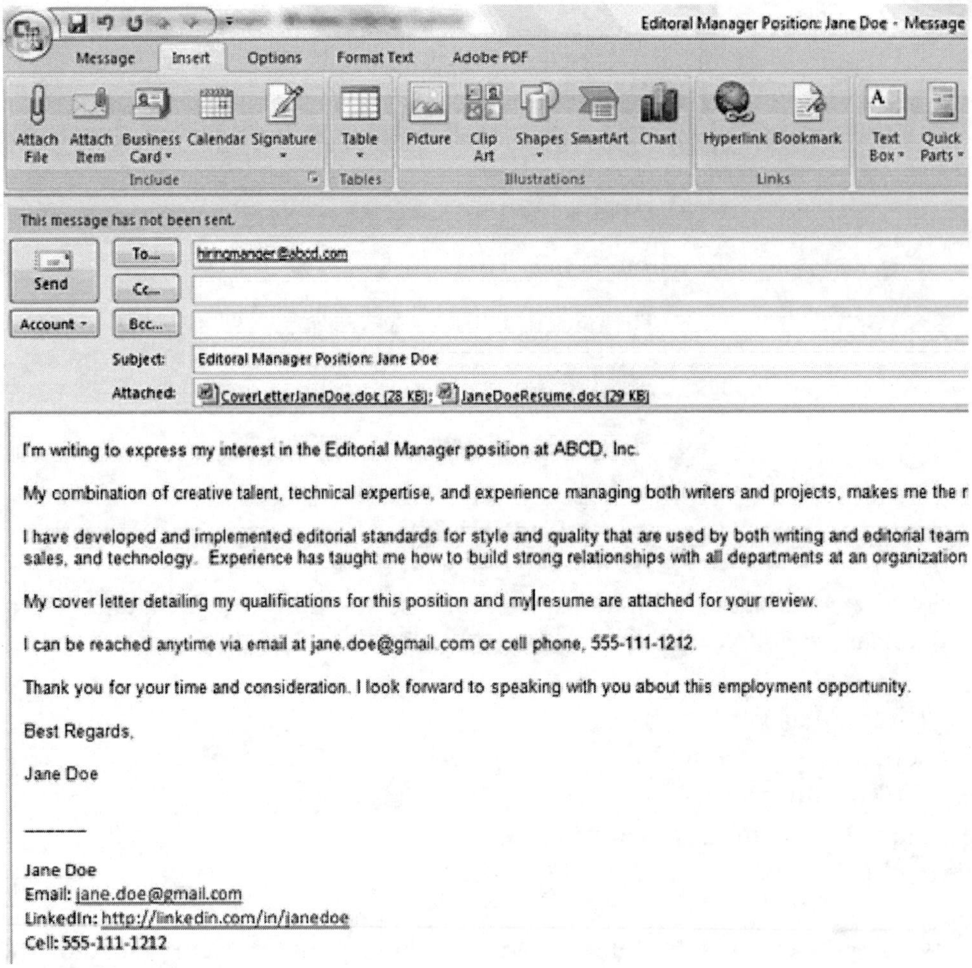

Message | Insert | Options | Format Text | Adobe PDF

Attach File | Attach Item | Business Card | Calendar | Signature | Table | Picture | Clip Art | Shapes | SmartArt | Chart | Hyperlink | Bookmark | Text Box | Quick Parts

Include | Tables | Illustrations | Links

This message has not been sent.

Send | Account |

To... | hiringmanager@abcd.com
Cc... |
Bcc... |
Subject: | Editoral Manager Position: Jane Doe
Attached: | CoverLetterJaneDoe.doc (28 KB); JaneDoeResume.doc (29 KB)

I'm writing to express my interest in the Editorial Manager position at ABCD, Inc.

My combination of creative talent, technical expertise, and experience managing both writers and projects, makes me the r

I have developed and implemented editorial standards for style and quality that are used by both writing and editorial team sales, and technology. Experience has taught me how to build strong relationships with all departments at an organization

My cover letter detailing my qualifications for this position and my resume are attached for your review.

I can be reached anytime via email at jane.doe@gmail.com or cell phone, 555-111-1212.

Thank you for your time and consideration. I look forward to speaking with you about this employment opportunity.

Best Regards,

Jane Doe

————

Jane Doe
Email: jane.doe@gmail.com
LinkedIn: http://linkedin.com/in/janedoe
Cell: 555-111-1212

FIGURE 2.8

2.2.1.10 EXPLAIN AN EMPLOYMENT GAP

When you have recent gaps in your resume, whether from being laid-off and out of work, taking time out from the workplace to spend with your family, traveling, going back to school, or for any reason, your cover letter gives you an opportunity to explain an employment gap.
When you address the gap in your cover letter, the hiring manager will be aware that there's an explanation for you being out of the workforce. If you did volunteer work or consulting you can mention it. However, you don't need to provide a lengthy explanation - be brief and to the point.

Do keep in mind, that given the job market, there are many resumes with gaps, so deciding whether to reference the employment gap is optional.

If the gap was in the past, you don't need to mention it. In fact, you don't need to include all your experience on your resume, especially if you have been in the workforce for years. It's acceptable to limit the "years of experience" you include on your resume to fifteen years when seeking a managerial or professional position and ten years when looking for other positions.

Figure 2.9

2.2.1.11 COVER LETTER CORRESPONDENCE

Cover letter presentation matters as much as what you include. When writing cover letters it's important to use a basic font that is easy to read. Depending on the hiring process your cover letter may be viewed in an applicant tracking system or other online hiring system. Those systems work best reading simple text rather than fancy formatting.

It's also important for the hiring manager to be able to easily read your resume. Using a basic 12 point font will ensure that your cover letter is easy to read. Basic fonts like Arial, Verdana, and Times New Roman work well. Don't forget to leave space between paragraphs and to proof your letter before you send or upload it. Do remember that your cover letter fonts should match your resume.

Main **differences** between e-mail and hard copy correspondence:

Format: your **signature block** (address, etc.) goes below your name in e-mail, while it goes at the top of the page on hard copy.

E-mail requires a **subject line** logical to the recipient. E-mail subject lines can make or break whether your e-mail is opened and read. Hard copy can have a subject line too, but it's on the letter (after recipient's address block and before "Dear...," and it's seen after the letter is opened.

Signature: Of course you won't have a handwritten signature on e-mail, but don't forget this on hard copy.

All cover letters should:

Explain why you are sending a resume.
Don't send a resume without a cover letter.

Don't make the reader guess what you are asking for; be specific: Do you want a summer internship opportunity, or a permanent position at graduation; are you inquiring about future employment possibilities?

Tell specifically how you learned about the position or the organization — a flyer posted in your department, a web site, a family friend who works at the organization. It is appropriate to mention the name of someone who suggested that you write.

Convince the reader to look at your resume.
The cover letter will be seen first.
Therefore, it must be very well written and targeted to that employer.

Call attention to elements of your background — education, leadership, experience — that are relevant to a position you are seeking. Be as specific as possible, using examples.

Reflect your attitude, personality, motivation, enthusiasm, and communication skills.

Provide or refer to any information specifically requested in a job advertisement that might not be covered in your resume, such as availability date, or reference to an attached writing sample.

Indicate what you will do to follow-up.

In a letter of application — applying for an advertised opening — applicants often say something like "I look forward to hearing from you." However, if you have further contact info (e.g. phone number) and if the employer hasn't said "no phone calls," it's better to take the initiative to follow-up, saying something like, "I will contact you in the next two weeks to see if you require any additional information regarding my qualifications."

In a letter of inquiry — asking about the possibility of an opening — don't assume the employer will contact you. You should say something like, "I will contact you in two weeks to learn more about upcoming employment opportunities with (name of organization)." Then mark your calendar to make the call.

Page margins, font style and size

For hard copy, left and right page margins of one to 1.5 inches generally look good. You can adjust your margins to balance how your document looks on the page.

Use a font style that is simple, clear and commonplace, such as Times New Roman, Arial or Calibri. Font SIZES from 10-12 points are generally in the ballpark of looking appropriate. Keep in mind that **different font styles in the same point size are not the same size**. A 12-point Arial is larger than a 12-point Times New Roman.

If you are having trouble fitting a document on one page, sometimes a slight margin and/or font adjustment can be the solution.

Serif or sans serif? Sans (without) serif fonts are those like Arial and Calibri that don't have the small finishing strokes on the ends of each letter. There is a great deal of research and debate on the pros and cons of each. Short story: use what you like, within reason; note what employers use; generally sans serif fonts are used for on-monitor reading and serif fonts are used for lengthy print items (like books); serif fonts may be considered more formal. Test: ask someone to look at a document for five seconds; take away the document; ask the person what font was on the document; see if s/he even noticed the style. A too-small or too-large font gets noticed, as does a weird style.

Should your resume and cover letter font style and size match? It can be a nice touch to look polished. But it's also possible to have polished documents that are not in matching fonts. A significant difference in style and size might be noticed. Remember that you can have your documents reviewed through advising, and that might be a fine-tuning question you ask.

A Cover Letter Template (Style 1):

Your Contact Information
Name
Address
City, State, Zip Code
Phone Number
Email Address

Date

Employer Contact Information (if you have it)
Name
Title
Company
Address
City, State, Zip Code

Salutation
Dear Mr./Ms. Last Name, (leave out if you don't have a contact)

Body of Cover Letter
The body of your cover letter lets the employer know what position you are applying for, why the employer should select you for an interview, and how you will follow-up.

First Paragraph
The first paragraph of your letter should include information on why you are writing. Mention the position you are applying for and where you found the job listing. Include the name of a mutual contact, if you have one.

Middle Paragraph(s)
The next section of your cover letter should describe what you have to offer the employer. Mention specifically how your qualifications match the job you are applying for. Remember, you are interpreting your resume, not repeating it.

Final Paragraph
Conclude your cover letter by thanking the employer for considering you for the position. Include information on how you will follow-up.

Complimentary Close

Respectfully yours,

Signature

A Cover Letter Template (Style 2):

*(Hard copy: sender address and contact info at top. **Your address and the date can be left-justified, or centered**.)*

Your Street Address
City, State Zip Code
Telephone Number
E-mail Address

Month, Day, Year

Mr./Ms./Dr. FirstName LastName
Title
Name of Organization
Street or P. O. Box Address
City, State Zip Code

Dear Mr./Ms./Dr. LastName:

Opening paragraph: State why you are writing; how you learned of the organization or position, and basic information about yourself.

2nd paragraph: Tell why you are interested in the employer or type of work the employer does (Simply stating that you are interested does not tell why, and can sound like a form letter). Demonstrate that you know enough about the employer or position to relate your background to the employer or position. Mention specific qualifications which make you a good fit for the employer's needs. (Focus on what you can do for the employer, not what the employer can do for you.) This is an opportunity to explain in more detail relevant items in your resume. Refer to the fact that your resume is enclosed. Mention other enclosures if such are required to apply for a position.

3rd paragraph: Indicate that you would like the opportunity to interview for a position or to talk with the employer to learn more about their opportunities or hiring plans. State what you will do to follow up, such as telephone the employer within two weeks. If you will be in the employer's location and could offer to schedule a visit, indicate when. State that you would be glad to provide the employer with any additional information needed. Thank the employer for her/his consideration.

Sincerely,

(Your handwritten signature [on hard copy])

Your name typed
(In case of e-mail, your full contact info appears below your printed name [instead of at the top, as for hard copy], and of course there is no handwritten signature)

Enclosure(s) (refers to resume, etc.)

(Note: the contents of your letter might best be arranged into four paragraphs. Consider what you need to say and use good writing style.)

<u>**Sample Cover Letter A—Letter of Application, e-mail version**</u>

Subject line: *(logical to recipient!)* Application for sales representative for mid-Atlantic area

April 14, 2010

Mr. William Jackson
Employment Manager
Acme Pharmaceutical Corporation
13764 Jefferson Parkway
Roanoke, VA 24019
jackson@acmepharmaceutical.com

Dear Mr. Jackson:

From the Acme web site I learned about your need for a sales representative for the Virginia, Maryland, and North Carolina areas. I am very interested in this position with Acme Pharmaceuticals, and believe that my education and employment background are appropriate for the position.

You indicate that a requirement for the position is a track record of success in meeting sales goals. I have done this. After completion of my B.S. in biology, and prior to beginning my master's degree in marketing, I worked for two years as a sales representative with a regional whole foods company. My efforts yielded success in new business development, and my sales volume consistently met or exceeded company goals. I would like to repeat that success in the pharmaceutical industry, using my academic background in science and business. I will complete my M.S. in marketing in mid-May and will be available to begin employment in early June.

Attached is a copy of my resume, which more fully details my qualifications for the position.

I look forward to talking with you regarding sales opportunities with Acme Pharmaceuticals. Within the next week I will contact you to confirm that you received my e-mail and resume and to answer any questions you may have.

Thank you very kindly for your consideration.

Sincerely,
Layne A. Johnson
5542 Hunt Club Lane, #1
Blacksburg, VA 24060
(540) 555-8082
lajohnson@vt.edu

Resume attached as MS Word document *(assuming company web site instructed applicants to do this)*

<u>**Sample Cover Letter B—Letter of Application, e-mail version**</u>

Subject line: *(**logical to recipient!**)* Application for marketing research position #031210-528

March 14, 2010

Ms. Charlene Prince
Director of Personnel
Large National Bank Corporation
Roanoke, VA 24040
cprince@largebank.com

Dear Ms. Prince:

As I indicated in our telephone conversation yesterday, I would like to apply for the marketing research position (#031210-528) advertised in the March 12th *Roanoke Times and World News*. With my undergraduate research background, my training in psychology and sociology, and my work experience, I believe I could make a valuable contribution to Large National Bank Corporation in this position.

In May I will complete my B.S. in Psychology with a minor in Sociology at Virginia Tech. As part of the requirements for this degree, I am involved in a senior marketing research project that has given me experience interviewing and surveying research subjects and assisting with the analysis of the data collected. I also have completed a course in statistics and research methods.

My experience also includes working part-time as a bookkeeper in a small independent bookstore with an annual budget of approximately $150,000. Because of the small size of this business, I have been exposed to and participated in most aspects of managing a business, including advertising and marketing. As the bookkeeper, I produced monthly sales reports that allow the owner/buyer to project seasonal inventory needs. I also assisted with the development of ideas for special promotional events and calculated book sales proceeds after each event in order to evaluate its success.

I believe my combination of business experience and social science research training is an excellent match for the marketing research position you described. Enclosed is a copy of my resume with additional information about my qualifications. Thank you very much for your consideration. I look forward to receiving your reply.

Sincerely,
Alex Lawrence
250 Prices Fork Road
Blacksburg, VA 24060
(540) 555-1234
alex.lawrence@vt.edu

Resume attached as MS Word document

Sample Cover Letter C—Letter of Application, hard copy version

-2 Apartment Heights Dr.
Blacksburg, VA 24060
(540) 555-0101
abcd@vt.edu

February 22, 2011

Dr. Michelle Rhodes
Principal, Wolftrap Elementary School
1205 Beulah Road
Vienna, VA 22182

Dear Dr. Rhodes:

I enjoyed our conversation on February 18th at the Family and Child Development seminar on teaching elementary children and appreciated your personal input about balancing the needs of children and the community during difficult economic times. This letter is to follow-up about the Fourth Grade Teacher position as discussed at the seminar. I will complete my M.Ed. in Curriculum and Instruction at Virginia Tech in May 2011, and will be available for employment as soon as needed for the 2011-12 school year.

My teacher preparation program at Virginia Tech has included a full academic year of student teaching. Last semester I taught second grade and this semester am teaching fourth grade. These valuable experiences have afforded me the opportunity to:

- Develop lesson plans on a wide range of topics and varying levels of academic ability,
- Work with emotionally and physically challenged students in a total inclusion program,
- Observe and participate in effective classroom management approaches,
- Assist with parent-teacher conferences, and
- Complete in-service sessions on diversity, math and reading skills, and community relations.

My experience includes work in a private day care facility, Rainbow Riders Childcare Center, and in Virginia Tech's Child Development Laboratory. Both these facilities are NAEYC-accredited and adhere to the highest standards. At both locations, I led small and large group activities, helped with lunches and snacks, and implemented appropriate activities. Both experiences also provided me with extensive exposure to the implementation of developmentally appropriate activities and materials.

I enthusiastically look forward to putting my knowledge and experience into practice in the public school system. Next week I will be in Vienna, and I plan to call you then to answer any questions that you may have. I can be reached before then at (540) 555-7670. Thank you very much for your consideration.

Sincerely,
(handwritten signature)
Donna Harrington

Enclosure

Sample Cover Letter D—Letter of Application, hard copy version

1000 Terrace View Apts.
Blacksburg, VA 24060
(540) 555-4523
stevemason@vt.edu

March 25, 2010

Ms. Janice Wilson
Personnel Director
Anderson Construction Company
3507 Rockville Pike
Rockville, MD 20895

Dear Ms. Wilson:

I read in the March 24th *Washington Post* classified section of your need for a Civil Engineer or Building Construction graduate for one of your Washington, DC, area sites. I will be returning to the Washington area after graduation in May and believe that I have the necessary credentials for the project.

Every summer for the last five years I have worked at various levels in the construction industry. As indicated on my enclosed resume, I have worked as a general laborer, and moved up to skilled carpentry work, and last summer served as assistant construction manager on a two million dollar residential construction project.

In addition to this practical experience, I will complete requirements for my B.S. in Building Construction in May. As you may know, Virginia Tech is one of the few universities in the country that offers such a specialized degree for the construction industry. I am confident that my degree, along with my years of construction industry experience, make me an excellent candidate for your job.

The Anderson Construction Company projects are familiar to me, and my aspiration is to work for a company that has your excellent reputation. I would welcome the opportunity to interview with you. I will be in the Washington area during the week of April 12th and would be available to speak with you at that time. In the next week to ten days I will contact you to answer any questions you may have.

Thank you for your consideration.

Sincerely,
(handwritten signature)
Jesse Mason

Enclosure

Subject: _(logical to recipient!)_ Inquiry about software engineering position after completion of M.S. in computer engineering

December 12, 2009

Mr. Robert Burns
President, Template Division
MEGATEK Corporation
9845 Technical Way
Arlington, VA 22207
burns@megatek.com

Dear Mr. Burns:

Via online research in Hokies4Hire through Career Services at Virginia Tech, I learned of MEGATEK. Next May I will complete my master of science in computer engineering. From my research on your web site, I believe there would be a good fit between my skills and interests and your needs. I am interested in a software engineering position upon completion of my degree.

As a graduate student, I am one of six members on a software development team in which we are writing a computer-aided aircraft design program for NASA. My responsibilities include designing, coding, and testing of a graphical portion of the program which requires the use of ZX-WWG for graphics input and output. I have a strong background in CAD, software development, and engineering, and believe that these skills would benefit the designing and manufacturing aspects of template software. Enclosed is my resume with further background information.

My qualifications equip me to make a contribution to the project areas in which your division of MEGATEK is expanding efforts. I would appreciate the opportunity to discuss a position with you, and will contact you in a week or ten days to answer any questions you may have and to see if you need any other information from me. Thank you for your consideration.

Sincerely,
Morgan Stevens
123 Ascot Lane
Blacksburg, VA 24060
(540) 555-2556
mstevens@vt.edu

Resume attached as MS Word document

Sample Cover Letter F—Letter of Inquiry about Internship Opportunities, hard copy version

2343 Blankinship Road
Blacksburg, VA 24060
(540) 555-2233
StacyLeeGimble@vt.edu

January 12, 2010

Ms. Sylvia Range
Special Programs Assistant
Marion County Family Court Wilderness Challenge
303 Center Street
Marion, VA 24560

Subj: Wilderness Challenge internship position

Dear Ms. Range:

This semester I am a junior at Virginia Tech, working toward my bachelor's degree in family and child development. I am seeking an internship for this summer 2010, and while researching opportunities in the field of criminal justice and law, I found that your program works with juvenile delinquents. I am writing to inquire about possible internship opportunities with the Marion County Family Court Wilderness Challenge.

My work background and coursework have supplied me with many skills and an understanding of dealing with the adolescent community; for example:

- 10 hours per week as a volunteer hotline assistant for a local intervention center. After a 50-hour training program, I counseled teenagers about personal concerns and referred them, when necessary, to appropriate professional services for additional help.

- Residence hall assistant in my residence hall, which requires me to establish rapport with fifty residents and advise them on personal matters, as well as university policies. In addition, I develop social and educational programs and activities each semester for up to 200 participants.

My enclosed resume provides additional details about my background.

I will be in the Marion area during my spring break, March 6-10. I will call you next week to see if it would be possible to meet with you in early March to discuss your program.

Thank you for your consideration.

Sincerely,
(handwritten signature)
Stacy Lee Gimble

Encl.

Sample Cover Letter G—Information Seeking Letter, hard copy version

23 Roanoke Street
Blacksburg, VA 24060
(540) 555-1123
K.Walker@vt.edu

October 23, 2010

Mr. James G. Webb
Delon Hampton & Associates
800 K Street, N.W., Suite 720
Washington, DC 20001-8000

Dear Mr. Webb:

Next May I will complete my bachelor's degree in Architecture at Virginia Tech, and am researching employment opportunities in the Washington area. I obtained your name from Professor (last name) who teaches my professional seminar class this semester. S/he indicated that you had volunteered to provide highly motivated graduating students with career advice, and I hope that your schedule will permit you to allow me to ask for some of your time and advice. I am particularly interested in historic preservation and have done research on the DHA website to learn that your firm does work in this area. I am also interested in learning how the architects in your firm began their careers. My resume is enclosed simply to give you some information about my background and project work.

Within two weeks I will call you to arrange a time to speak to you by telephone or perhaps visit your office if that would be convenient. I will be in the Washington area during the week of November 22. I very much appreciate your time and consideration of my request, and I look forward to talking with you.

Sincerely,
(handwritten signature)
Kristen Walker

Encl.

2.2.1.12 AFTER INTERVIEW | THANK-YOU LETTERS | FOLLOW-UP

Following an interview, promptly (within 2 business days) write the interviewer a letter expressing appreciation and thanks for the interview.

The purpose of this letter is to:

- Show appreciation for the employer's interest in you.

- Reiterate your interest in the position and in the organization.

- Review or remind the employer about your qualifications for the position. If you thought of something you forgot to mention in the interview, mention it in your follow-up / thank-you letter.

- Demonstrate that you have good manners and know to write a thank-you letter.

- Follow up with any information the employer may have asked you to provide after the interview.

Thank-you letters can be hard copy typed, handwritten or e-mailed.

Hard copy not-handwritten are most formal and are appropriate after an interview.

Handwritten are more personal, and can be appropriate for brief notes to a variety of individuals you may have met during an on-site interview.

E-mail is appropriate, particularly as a supplement (i.e. do both e-mail and hard copy) when that has been your means of contact with the person you want to thank, or if your contact has expressed a preference for e-mail, or you know your contact is travelling and will not have access to hard copy mail in a timely fashion.

Before your interview ended, your interviewer should have informed you of the organization's follow-up procedures — from whom (same person who interviewed you, someone else), by what means (phone, e-mail, etc.), and when you would hear again from the organization. If the interviewer did not tell you, and you did not ask, use your follow-up / thank-you letter to ask.

If more than a week has passed beyond the date when you were told you would hear something from the employer (and barring some major event in the news like a merger or acquisition or other event that would be taking employees' attention), call or e-mail to politely inquire about the status of the organization's decision-making process. Someone (or something) or an unexpected circumstance may be holding up the process. A polite inquiry shows that you are still interested in the organization and may prompt the employer to get on schedule with a response. In your inquiry, mention the following: name of the person who interviewed you, time and place of the interview, position for which you are applying (if known), and ask the status of your application.

400C Hunter Ridge
Blacksburg, VA 24060
(540) 555-1111
boles@vt.edu

October 26, 2010

Ms. Glenna Wright
Human Resources Manager
Fashion Department Store
2000 Line Drive
Fairfax, VA 22030

Dear Ms. Wright:

Thank you so much for your time and the privilege of having an interview with you yesterday, October 25, during your recruiting visit to Virginia Tech. The management trainee program you outlined sounds both challenging and rewarding and I look forward to your decision concerning an on-site visit.

As mentioned during the interview, I will be graduating in December with a B.S. in Fashion Merchandising. Through my education and experience I've gained many skills, as well as an understanding of retailing concepts and dealing with the general public. I have worked seven years in the retail industry in various positions from sales associate to assistant department manager. I think my education and work experience would complement Fashion's management trainee program.

I have enclosed a copy of my college transcript and a list of references that you requested.

Thank you again for the opportunity to be considered by Fashion Department Store. The interview served to reinforce my strong interest in becoming a part of your management team. I can be reached at (540) 555-1111 or by e-mail at boles@vt.edu should you need additional information.

Sincerely,

Marianne Boles

Enclosures

Sample Letter I—Thank You for On-Site Interview

170 Roanoke Street
Blacksburg, VA 24060
(540) 555-6241
JRichardson@vt.edu

March 3, 2011

Ms. Patricia Smith
Personnel Manager
Sheldon E-Solutions
1212 Lark Lane
Richmond, VA 23230

Dear Ms. Smith:

Thank you for the opportunity to visit with you and see your facilities last Wednesday. Both the interview and the tour made for an exciting and complete day.

I was so very impressed with your warehousing procedures. Mr. Allen was so thorough in explaining your process to me, and I will be corresponding directly with him to express my appreciation. Incidentally, the process you use is quite similar to one I have been researching through an independent study this term. Perhaps I can share my final report with you and Mr. Allen.

The expense report you requested is enclosed.

Again, thank you for your hospitality during my time in Richmond and for all your efforts to arrange my visit. Having seen your operation, I am all the more enthused about the career opportunity that Sheldon E-Solutions offers. I look forward to your decision.
Sincerely,

Jan Richardson
Enclosure

2.2.1.13 ACKNOWLEDGING OFFER | DECLINE OFFER | REQUEST EXTENSION

Courtesy dictates that you acknowledge a written job offer, even if you are not ready to accept or decline it. Take note of the details of the offer, as specified in your offer letter, and respond appropriately.

You may respond verbally and in writing; whether via e-mail or hard-copy depending on the pattern and mode of communication you have had with the employer, and instructions from the employer.

Items to remember:

- Thank the employer for the opportunity presented.
- If you understand the terms of the offer, indicate that. If you don't, ask for clarification.
- A smart employer will know that you may be considering various employment options and need to make a deliberative decision; you may need to compare the offer to another pending offer.
- However, you might need to make a decision before you know if you will receive another offer.

Sample Letter J—Acknowledging a Job Offer, neither Accepting nor Declining

444 University Road
Blacksburg, VA 24060
(540) 555-9876
gguthrie@vt.edu

February 1, 20xx

Mr. Chris Afton
Grand Hotel Inc.
8899 Jefferson Street
Roanoke, VA 24022

Dear Mr. Afton:

This is to acknowledge your letter offering me the catering and sales representative position with Grand Hotel, Incorporated. Thank you very much for offering me this exciting opportunity. I understand the terms of the offer, and will be able to give you my response by your requested deadline of February 16. I appreciate your allowing me ample time to consider your offer so as to be sure my decision will be in the best interests of both my career goals and the needs of your organization.

In the meantime, I will be in contact with you if I have any additional questions, and I will respond promptly should you need to reach me. Again, thank you so much for this wonderful opportunity.

Yours truly,

(your signature)

George Guthrie

If you choose to decline a job offer, do so courteously, in writing, after making a phone call.

Never say anything negative in writing about the employer, even if you had a negative experience. If you had a very negative experience, it is best to share this information with Career Services.

A decision to decline an offer is usually based on the fact that another offer is a better fit for your interests and goals. It is fine to state this, without giving details about why the declined offer is not a fit.

It is not necessary to state whose offer you accepted, but you may do so if you wish. Remember that this employer may be a contact for you in the future. Maintain the relationship with professional, courteous interactions.

Sample Letter J—Declining a Job Offer

900 Town Road
Blacksburg, VA 24060
(540) 555-9009
email: myname@vt.edu

April 20, 2010

Dr. Joan Swietzer
Citizens Network for Foreign Affairs
343 Third Street, NW
Washington, DC 20201-0343

Dear Dr. Swietzer:

Thank you very much for your telephone call and letter offering me the position of Assistant Project Coordinator with the Citizens Network for Foreign Affairs. While I believe firmly in the mission of your organization and appreciate the challenging opportunity you offer, I have had another offer which I believe more closely aligns with my current career goals and interests. Therefore, although it was a difficult decision, as I explained when we spoke by phone this morning, I must decline your offer. I do appreciate all the courtesy and hospitality extended to me by your office, and I wish you the best in your endeavors.

In the position I have accepted with Public Policy Watch, I will occasionally be on Capitol Hill to attend hearings and monitor legislation, so I hope we can get together again and talk about common interests.

Best regards,

(your signature)
Chris Hancock

In some cases you may need more time than the employer has allowed for your decision.

What to do:

You may ask for an extension; the employer does not have to grant it.

Make sure you have a concrete and appropriate reason for asking for an extension. Expecting to hear soon from another employer with whom you've interviewed is a legitimate reason. If you just hoping to get more interviews, that's not a concrete reason.

Don't wait until the last minute to ask for an extension; this looks like you don't think ahead and may indicate that you might behave the same way on the job.

Be tactful and diplomatic in your wording. You will need to explain your reasons to the employer. For example, if you have an upcoming, previously scheduled interview with another employer, you may explain that it is important to you to keep your commitment to the other employer, and that in order to make the best decision; you need to attend the other interview.

For the sake of speed, phone the employer to discuss the situation. For the record, you should follow up in writing. Since this is a request that needs to be handled quickly, e-mail is probably the best method to confirm your request.

<u>**Sample Email —Requesting an Extension of Deadline to Accept or Decline Job Offer**</u>

(sample of e-mail)

(March 1, 201x)

Dr. Thomas G. Jones
Oregon Department of Fish and Wildlife
2300 Main Street
Portland, OR 90001
tgjonesemailaddress@agency.gov

Dear Dr. Jones:

Thank you for your telephone call and letter that I received yesterday offering me the position of wildlife biologist with the Oregon Department of Fish and Wildlife. I am excited about the opportunity this position offers both in terms of job duties and location, and I very much appreciate your confidence in offering me the job.

You asked that I make a decision by next week on March 7. This is an important decision, and unfortunately I do not have all the information I need in order to make this decision by that date. To confirm our phone conversation of this afternoon, I am asking you to consider whether it would be possible for me to supply you with my decision by March 28. I would very much appreciate such an extension, and assure you that I will be able to make a firm decision by that date.

Thank you very much for your consideration of my request.

Sincerely,
Hannah Lenke
Fish and Wildlife Sciences & Biology double-major | Virginia Tech
343 Jefferson Street
Blacksburg, VA 24060
(540) 555-8754
HannahLenke@vt.edu

If this were sent as hard-copy, your address and contact info would appear at the top. Since this type of request needs to be handled quickly, most likely you would communicate verbally and use e-mail for confirmation in writing.

2.2.1.14 ACCEPTANCE OF A JOB OFFER

Accepting a job offer (in addition to cause for celebration!) ethically obligates you to:

- Keep your word.
- Cease job search efforts.

If you have accepted a co-op or internship position, e-mail your co-op / internship advisor.

- Promptly notify other employers who have communicated to you that you are under consideration that you must withdraw your name from their consideration.

- First means of notice: a courteous phone call. Make every effort to speak to your contact in person rather than leaving a voice mail message for this purpose.

- Follow up your phone call in writing; please review Sample Letter K. Use e-mail or hard copy depending on the pattern and mode of communication you have had with the employer. Hard copy is more formal; if you have already had an interview with the employer, that more formal means of communication may be advisable.

Failing to notify employers that you are withdrawing from the job search is discourteous, and potentially dishonest. It's essentially leaves the employer with a misperception that you are still interested in the job.

Sample Letter K—Accepting a Job Offer

1234 College Road
Blacksburg, VA 24060
(540) 555-0000
firslastname@vt.edu

March 1, 20xx

Mr. Johnathon P. Summers
Summers Fruit Company
1678 Plantation Road
Atlanta, GA 46201

Dear Mr. Summers:

Thank you for your offer of employment as a horticultural associate at your Fruitville, Florida, site. As we discussed on the phone this morning, I am delighted to accept your offer and look forward to beginning work with Summers Fruit Company.

You indicated that I will be receiving a salary of $_____ per year, and will have initial duties reporting to Andrea Caruso. As your offer stated, I will begin work on August 1st. In mid-July, after relocating to the area, I will call you to see what information or materials I may need before August 1st. In the meantime, please let me know if I can provide you with any information.

Again, thank you for offering me this exciting opportunity. I am very enthused about beginning my career with you after graduation.

Sincerely,

(your signature)

Jason Banyon

Ethical Issues related to accepting a Job Offer:

- Your acceptance of a job offer is binding.
- Don't accept a job offer, even verbally, until you are certain you are committed.
- Don't back out after accepting; that's called reneging, and is unethical.
- An employer should never pressure you to renege on another employer.
- Once you have accepted a job offer, notify any other employers with whom you are in discussion about employment that you are no longer a candidate. Cancel any upcoming interviews by courteously explaining that you have accepted another job offer.

2.2.1.15 YOU HAVE ONE OFFER, BUT YOU ARE HOPING FOR ANOTHER

The situation: Not uncommon for job seekers:

You have an offer from employer B.

You've gone through the interview process with employer A, and you're hoping for, and perhaps expecting an offer. You really want the job with employer A.

B has given you a deadline, perhaps two weeks from the offer date.

You haven't heard from A, and you might not hear until near or after B's deadline.

You'd rather work for A, but B has given you a great offer, and you don't want to turn that down if A doesn't want you.

What to do?

The solution:

First, never accept an offer and then back out later.
That's called reneging, and it's considered highly unethical and inappropriate and is very disturbing to employers (and they do talk to each other). You may hear opinions that it's okay. It's not. Ask yourself what your ethical standards are.)

Without delay, call employer A and let your contact know the situation. Keep your information simple and factual regarding the offer from B. You don't have to mention organization B's name, but you might be asked. Reiterate to employer A that you really want to work for A. Ask where you stand in the evaluation process and if there is any possibility to have definitive information from A before B's deadline, and if not, when that might be.

Your goals: Diplomatically learn more about your status with A, let A know your interest in them, and perhaps stimulate A to speed up their process if they really want you.

Next, without delay, call employer B. Express appreciation for the offer. Indicate that you don't yet have all the information you need to make your decision. (Good organizations will want you to make a well-informed decision and they are aware job seekers are looking at multiple options.)

If A will give you a final decision by or shortly after B's deadline, you have the option to ask B for a deadline extension — just don't wait until the last minute to ask. B can say yes or no to your request; you won't know until you ask.

Your goals: Maintain your good relationship with B, and perhaps gain some time to make your decision.

Bottom line: Be as honest as you can while being diplomatic. Treat everyone with respect; maintaining good relationships with organizations and individuals (who may change organizations) will serve your long-term career success.

Need more help sorting out your individual situation?

Consult a Career Services advisor — via walk-in advising or an appointment. They are there to help you sort through these kinds of situations.

2.3 RESUME

A **resume** is a summary of your experiences and skills relevant to the field of work you are entering. It highlights your accomplishments to show a potential employer that you are qualified for the work you want. It is not a biography of everything you have done. Its purpose is to get you an interview. A resume can (and often should) reflect more than just your paid work experience. Current students, in particular, should consider including the details of your more important extracurricular, volunteer and leadership experiences. Tailor separate resumes to fit each career field in which you are job searching. Some people create slightly different resumes tailored to each job opening. Remember that you can attend a resume workshop or have your resume critiqued at the career center of your college or university.

2.3.1 WHAT IS A RESUME?

Depending on whom you ask, a resume may be viewed as the single most important vehicle to securing your next job, or it may be viewed as an unnecessary nuisance.

In actuality, a resume is a professional introduction meant to encourage a one-on-one interview situation; an opportunity for communication that can lead to a job offer.

It is a rare candidate who is hired by his or her resume alone. It is just as rare to be offered an interview without one.

A resume is often the first line of contact. It establishes a first impression of a potential job candidate's skills, background and hiring value. If written well, this impression can be a positive one, offering the reader a sense of the candidate's "fit" for the position and company being targeted. If written really well, it may convince the reader that the job candidate is the person most ideally suited for the job. When coupled with an effective cover letter, the resume can be a very strong marketing tool.

Preparing a resume may be seen as a nuisance, but having a well-constructed, well-designed resume is an important part of your job search. Consider that for each available job opening there may be as many as 100 to 1000 resumes submitted. If your resume fails to adequately represent your qualifications (for the specific position), fails to establish your hiring value over competing candidates, or is difficult to follow, your ability to compete against those other 100 to 1000 professionals vying for the same position will be greatly diminished.

If your resume secures an interview, then it has done its job. If it sets you ahead of the competition in the mind of your interviewer, then it has given you a distinct advantage and gone beyond its main objective. Good job, because that should be your goal.

A great resume does what all good marketing pieces do: it sells the "consumer" (the potential employer or hiring manager) on the "product" (you).

Like it or not, the act of looking for employment is a function of sales and marketing. The product you are "selling" is you, and the "customer" (the person you hope will "buy" the product) has unique needs and interests. This customer (potential employer) needs to be sold on the fact that you have what it takes to get the job done, that you will meet or exceed the needs and expectations of the position, and you will be worth the compensation.

The reader of your resume is going to want to know how you are going to solve his or her problems, and they are going to give your resume a whopping 15 seconds, or less, to sell you. 15 seconds is the average time a hiring manager will spend "reading" a new resume - before giving it a potential "yes" or "no" response.

2.3.2 PREPARATION IS KEY

In preparing your resume, the more you know about the position you are targeting, the better. If you know the company's missions and goals, if you understand the needs and expectations of the position, if you recognize the target company's "concerns," if you understand who comprises the company's customer base or target market... and you (and your unique skills and experience) can meet these needs and expectations (you have accurately assessed your own value and are able to communicate how your skills, experience and contributions have benefited employers in the past), then you will have the material necessary to create an effective marketing piece.

As in any type of marketing collateral, it is important to present the information so that it captures your reader's interest quickly. Your goal is to encourage the reader to stay with your document as long as possible. Your chance for a more detailed reading increases when you give the reader information which he or she most wants to secure, early in the document.

One of the best ways to accomplish this is to create a Summary Section at the beginning of your resume. A Summary Section highlights for your reader those personal and professional skills you possess that are relevant and valuable to the position you are targeting and allow you to excel in your chosen field and position.

Items and skills of greatest importance (from your readers' viewpoint) should be listed in priority, supporting an impression of both "fit" and potential success. In addition, these should be aspects of your background that set you apart from your competing candidates, particularly candidates with skill sets similar to your own.
You are, in effect, showing your reader how you will solve their problems - better than the competition - and why interviewing you will be a worthwhile expenditure of their time.

2.3.3 FOR WHOM YOU ARE WRITING?

First, let us be very clear about one important fact: you are not writing a career autobiography. This is not about you, seriously. It is about how you can meet the needs, interests and expectations of your reader and this particular position, at this particular company. It is all about them: about what they need, what their hopes and expectations are, and how what you bring to the table will meet these expectations. It is all about how you will benefit them.

The interview stage will be your first opportunity to negotiate; when you will get a chance to discuss what you hope to get out of the deal. But right now, the only person who matters is your reader. They hold all the marbles.

When writing your resume, keep in mind what your reader needs to know. Listing information that will be of no value or benefit to the position you are targeting or the company in question, is just a waste of time and space.

And not only does the information have to have value (from your reader's point-of-view), but it should be interesting, so that your reader wants to keep reading. If the information or dialogue feels repetitive or lacks flow; you will quickly lose your reader's attention.

Check for redundancy in your statements. If the positions you have held are similar, then repeating the same functions, over and over, in ad nauseam detail, will lose your reader's interest (heard it, got it). However, never short-change your accomplishments.

Your potential employer is most interested in seeing how hiring you will benefit the company. But keep this in mind, as well: if it were your job to fill this position, how important would it be to you to hire the best person possible, knowing this decision will reflect back upon your own capabilities?

If you are dealing with a hiring manager or Human Resource (HR) director, you can bet this person has a lot riding on the fact that, if you are hired, you are the right person for the job. It is extremely expensive to recruit, interview, hire and train, only to let an employee go and start the whole process over again. It is the HR director's job to make sure the right person is hired the first time.

All parties involved want to know the right hiring decision is being made. Make it your job to assure them that hiring you is a very good idea. The most effective way to achieve this is by identifying how your efforts and contributions have benefited employers in the past. Take credit for your participation and accomplishments. Know the quantitative results of your efforts (numbers, figures, dollar amounts, and percentages) wherever possible. While aspects of your background may seem minor or of little value to you, they may be seen as a valuable asset to those looking to fill a need.

2.3.4 THE LAYOUT OF YOUR RESUME

The layout of your resume is extremely important. Your resume needs to maintain a "clean" and professional appearance (remember, it is representing you!). It should allow the reader to access the information quickly, even at a glance.

Neat margins, adequate "white space" between groupings, and indenting to highlight text all aid ease of reference and retention of the material. Use bolding and italics sparingly. Overuse of these features can actually diminish their effectiveness of promoting the material they are intended highlight, and can also reduce overall readability.

Your contact information (how the reader can reach you) is essentially the most important information in the entire document. Make certain your name, address, phone number, and e-mail address are clearly visible and at the top of your document (from habit, this is where your reader will look for this information - do not make them search for it).

If your resume is more than one page in length, be certain that your name is on these secondary pages, in case the sheets become separated.

The standards for resume length have changed. It used to be typical for resumes to be no more than one-page in length. For candidates with years of experience, having held multiple positions, or having worked with multiple companies, or who have outstanding achievements to present, this one-page restriction can result in a document that is unreadable, looks "squashed," or utilizes a font size so small that the reader is forced to squint (no, they won't bother). The one-page standard no longer holds true.

Use as much space as you need to concisely, accurately, and effectively communicate your skills, history, achievements, and accomplishments - as these relate to the position and company being targeted. A two-page document, if presented well, will not diminish the effectiveness of your marketing strategy, as long as the information you provide is relevant and valuable to your reader's needs, goals and interests.

A three-page resume is requiring much of your reader's time (and patience), and may not be as effective as a more concise presentation. In fact, your reader may wonder if you have difficulty conveying your value and are unable to create a concise and powerful presentation.

In academic fields and European markets, it may be necessary to go over two pages in length, because additional detail and information is required. But only provide this much information if you feel it will be beneficial and if you are certain your reader will agree with you.

An overly long presentation may leave the reader wondering if you believe their time is not valuable. Remember, by creating something in writing, you are demanding the reader's time and attention. This is fine – just do not waste their time.

Document, **in detail**, the most recent 10 to15 years of your employment and/or experience. Longer if the most recent position extends back 10 years or more. Be certain to highlight growth and advancement in any company where multiple positions were held, including identification of promotions and increases in responsibility.

List prior positions in decreasing detail, unless a previous position more effectively represents your skills and experience relevant to the position and company you are currently targeting.

You want to entice you reader into wanting to meet you (the interview) **to learn more**. Current history and recently utilized skills will hold the most value.

Remember, you will have an opportunity to expand on the information provided in your resume during the interview. So, in your résumé: establish your qualifications, indicate the benefits of hiring you, and entice your reader to want to learn more, through a one-on-one interview.

2.3.5 PHOTOCOPY, FAX, AND SCAN

You can never be certain what your recipient may do with your resume once he or she is in receipt of it. Therefore, you want to make sure your resume can hold up to various processes such as faxing, scanning or photocopying.

Because of this, it is also a good idea to bring along fresh copies of your resume to each interview. Many interview sessions are held by multiple interviewers, and each interviewer should have a clean copy of your resume presentation (not a photocopied version).

Having a clean copy of your resume with you can also help if you if you are required to complete a job application or formal company documents.

A resume will not, typically, get you a job (well, it has happened, but it is extremely rare), but it can secure your chances of being seen and interviewed for a position or company that interests you - just as it can cause you to be passed over in favor of a candidate who offers a better presentation of what he or she has to offer.

It is often your first opportunity to make a company aware of you and all you have to offer.

As with any type of marketing campaign, use your resume as one tool in your job search. Continue to network, improve your interviewing skills, and use every avenue available to you to better your chances and opportunities.

And, when you have secured that next position, do this all over again. Always be prepared for the next opportunity. Keep your resume up-to-date and stay career fit.

2.3.6 TYPES OF RESUME

The format for a **chronological resume** is by far the most common form of resume in use today. The chronological resume is best suited for entry-level job-seekers or those who have stayed in the same field. Occasionally, alumni who are changing careers or re-entering the work force after a prolonged absence, or job-seekers with varied work experiences and accomplishments may find that a **functional resume** is more appropriate. A functional resume is one that is not job specific. In other words, you can write up a resume with your name, address, contact information, your goals, education, previous employers and personal references and use this resume.

2.3.6.1 THE CHRONOLOGICAL RESUME

Here are the key components of a standard chronological resume:

Identification

It is essential that a potential employer can reach you. This section should include your name, address, phone number(s), and e-mail address. If a college student, this section might also include a school address and a permanent home address.

Job Objective

A job objective is optional and should only be included for new college grads and those changing careers. Otherwise, use your cover letter to show your career interests and job objective. If you do use an objective, make sure your objective explains the kind of work you want to do, and keep it between two to four typed lines.

Key Accomplishments

Some resume experts are suggesting adding a section that highlights your key accomplishments and achievements. Think of this section as an executive summary of your resume; identify key accomplishments that will grab the attention of an employer.

This section should summarize (using nouns as keywords and descriptors) your major accomplishments and qualifications.

This section can also be labeled "Professional Profile," "Summary of Accomplishments," "Key Skills," "Summary of Qualifications," "Qualifications Summary," or "Qualifications."

Education

For new college grads, this entry should be your next. For others with full-time work experience, this section should follow your experience section.

This section should include school(s) attended (including years of attendance), majors/minors, degrees, and honors and awards received.

For new grads only: There appears to be a growing trend of employers wanting your GPA in this section. If you decide to do so, make sure to use the GPA that puts you in the best light -- either overall GPA, school or college GPA, or major GPA.

Professional Experience

This section can also be labeled "Experience, "Work History," or "Employment." Using experience is especially good for new college grads because experience is broader than work history, allowing you to include major school projects that showcase your skills and abilities.

This section should include company name, your job title, dates of employment, and major accomplishments. List experiences in reverse chronological order, starting with your most current experience.

List your accomplishments in bullet format (rather than paragraph format). Avoid discussing job duties or responsibilities.

If you don't have a lot of career-related job experience, consider using transferable skills to better highlight your work experience.

Finally, make sure to make use of action verbs when describing your accomplishments.

Affiliations/Interests

This section is optional; include only if you have room on your resume for it. Items from this section are often used as an ice-breaker by interviewers looking to start an interview on an informal basis.

This section should only include professional memberships and non-controversial activities/interests.

References

Many experts say this section is optional, but if you have room, include it. If nothing else, this section signals the end of your resume.

This section should only include a statement saying references are available upon request.

Do **not** include the names of your references on your resume.

2.3.6.2 THE FUNCTIONAL RESUME

Among jobseekers who should consider a functional format:

- Those with very diverse experiences that don't add up to a clear-cut career path
- College students with minimal experience and/or experience unrelated to their chosen career field.
- Career-changers who wish to enter a field very different from what all their previous experience points to.
- Those with gaps in their work history, such as homemakers who took time to raise and family and now wish to return to the workplace. For them, a chronological format can draw undue attention to those gaps, while a functional resume enables them to portray transferable skills attained through such activities as domestic management and volunteer work.
- Military transitioners entering a different field from the work they did in the military.
- Job-seekers whose predominate or most relevant experience has been unpaid, such as volunteer work or college activities (coursework, class projects, extracurricular organizations, and sports).
- Those who performed very similar activities throughout their past jobs who want to avoid repeating those activities in a chronological job listing.
- Job-seekers looking for a position for which a chronological listing would make them look "overqualified."
- Older workers seeking to deemphasize a lengthy job history.

If you can look at a chronological resume without a stated career objective and know exactly what field the jobseeker is headed toward and would be good at, then the chronological format probably is working just fine. But if you can't guess what the jobseeker wants to do and would be good at by looking at the chronology of past jobs, a functional format may be indicated.

The functional format also can work well for college students because it allows skills attained from experiences other than paid employment to be listed within the skills clusters. For example, one student chose leadership as one of her skills clusters, and she listed the following supporting experiences, none of them paid employment:

EXAMPLE 2: An example of leadership on a resume.

Leadership

- o Selected as president-elect of Omicron Delta Kappa honorary and vice president of Phi Eta Sigma honorary
- o Acquainted new students with campus as orientation leader
- o Serve as president of residence hall on Residence Hall Council
- o Function as vice president for intellectual development and assistant recruitment chair for social sorority

It's true that functional formats have been the subject of some employer backlash in recent years. Some employers are unaccustomed to the functional format, and they may become confused or even irritated by functional resumes. Recruiters/headhunters particularly disdain functional formats, so this approach should never be used if you are primarily targeting recruiters with your job search. Employers in conservative fields, such as banking, finance, and law are not big fans of functional formats, nor are international employers. Functional formats also are not acceptable on many online job boards.

Some employers like to know what you did in each job. One solution is to structure your resume in a mostly functional format but include a bare-bones work history in reverse chronological order, creating what is variously known as a chrono-functional, hybrid, or combination format. Such a work-history section need include only job title, name and location of employer, and dates of employment. You don't need to list what you did in each job because that information already is listed in your functional section.

To make your functional resume as reader-friendly as possible for employers, include as much context as you can within each functional description. That way, the employer has a better idea of which skill aligns with which job. In the above leadership-skills example, for instance, the student tells where she demonstrated each skill, thus making helping the employer connect her skills with the experience that produced those skills.

If you're unsure whether a functional resume is right for you, try it both ways and show the two formats to people in the field you wish to enter. See which one they feel presents your skills more effectively.

2.3.6.3 SAMPLE RESUME

SAMPLE CHRONOLOGICAL RESUME A

YOUR NAME
yourname@bc.edu (no hyperlink/line), 617-656-0000
Your Boston College address here, Chestnut Hill, MA 02467
Your home address here, Any Town, CA 01000

EDUCATION
Boston College   Chestnut Hill, MA
College of Arts and Sciences (optional *full, formal* name of school you are in)
Bachelor of Arts /Science in Major Minor (if you have one)   anticipated May 201x
GPA 3.xx (incl. GPA if > 3.00, do NOT round up)

Honors/Awards: Dean's List, Golden Key, AHANA Honor Roll
Relevant courses (optional) (if applicable - no more than 4-5 upper level classes)

Abroad University, City, Country Spring   Semester, 201x
Studied (courses/subjects included)
EXPERIENCE
Name of Organization City, State   Start date - end date
Job title
- Describe any accomplishments that you achieved at your job
- Explain what you did, how you did it, why you did it, and what the results were
- Whenever possible, quantify the number of people/items/data that you worked with
  (Use present tense for verbs describing jobs that you are currently performing)

Name of Organization City, State   Start date - end date
Job title
- Describing Accomplishments: Result + Action + Problem/Project = good bullet point
- **Sample vague bullet point**: Assisted with general upkeep and organization of homeless shelter
- **Sample good bullet points:** Prepared and served meals to 50 homeless male residents; Maintained organization of supply closet and distributed resources to residents as needed; Acted as a liaison between program participants and staff members.

VOLUNTEER EXPERIENCE and/or ACTIVITIES
Name of first Organization City, State   Start date - end date
Title
- Focus on a few key skills that your industry is looking for, and demonstrate how you used those skills through the description of the tasks/projects you accomplished at your job.

Name of Second Organization (brief description if necessary) City, State Start Date - end date
Title
- Remember to be consistent; punctuation at the end of the phrases is not necessary unless you are using paragraph formatting.

ACTIVITIES Section: List each organization (add an action verb phrase describing an acquired skill if you have space)

SKILLS

Computers: Microsoft Excel, PowerPoint, Word, and any other relevant computer skills or languages

Language: List all languages you are fluent or proficient in or currently studying, if listed as fluent, should be able to conduct interview in that language.

SAMPLE CHRONOLOGICAL RESUME B

Christopher O'Connell
coconnell@bc.edu · (cell) 617-656-1234

Boston College, Hardy House   14 Clark Street
Newton Centre, MA 02462
                                        Bayside, NY 13790

EDUCATION
Boston College, College of Arts and Sciences; Chestnut Hill, MA
Bachelor of Science in Psychology, May 2010
Honors Program; plan to research and write a thesis, complete focused program coursework

Benjamin Cardoza High School; Bayside, NY
High School Diploma, June 2006
Captain, Varsity Men's Crew

WORK EXPERIENCE
Benjamin Cardoza High School; Bayside, NY

Bookkeeper   Summer 2006
- Maintained account records of 4,000 student body school, including general ledger, accounts payable/receivable; prepared 370 bi-weekly payroll checks along with school accountant
- Analyzed class selections and times data to create 4,000 individual daily schedules for Students

Long Island Medical Group; Garden City, NY
Administrative Assistant   June 2005 - May 2006
- Verified and scheduled patient appointments for seven doctors; screened emergency situations to determine if visit was needed in order to keep doctor on schedule as much as possible
- Maintained over 5,000 patient files for doctor review before patient appointment; filed incoming lab results and notified doctor of any unusual reports

ACTIVITIES
- BC Men's Crew Team; devote 20 hours per week to practice during height of season
- 4Boston; volunteered four hours per week at the Jackson Mann Community Center Pre-school Program; acted as an aide for lead teacher
- Campus School Volunteer; spend five hours bi-weekly with a moderate special needs student

SKILLS
PC and Mac; Microsoft Word, Excel

INTERESTS
Mountain biking, cross country skiing, travel to Ireland, chess

SAMPLE CHRONOLOGICAL RESUME C

Mark Stomato   32 Frasure Ave., Malvern, PA 10324 (610) 552-0056

Boston College, Edmunds Room 122, Chestnut Hill, MA 02467 (617) 656-6601 stomato@bc.edu

OBJECTIVE
A Web design position within a Research and Design Division in a major consumer electronics organization.

EDUCATION
Boston College, Wallace E. Carroll School of Management; Chestnut Hill, MA
Bachelor of Science in Information Systems, May 2004
GPA 3.4, Dean's List First Honors

EXPERIENCE
General Electric Capital; Philadelphia, PA
Assistant Web Administrator   Summer 2003
- Created and implemented process to allow multiple groups and users to publish documents to a single source for an Intranet audience; increased lines of communication across 10 departments
- Designed Intranet database to record and track employee Total Quality Management practices; trained staff on usage of TQM reporting process, which also streamlined the entire process
- Constructed a database, for the Real Estate Department, to provide an organized method to track and contact
commercial developers and owners as part of Six Sigma quality project; raised awareness of business
- regional coverage and ensured targeting of only top players

Undergraduate Government at Boston College (UGBC), Boston College; Chestnut Hill, MA
Senator, Community Service Committee   Fall 2002 - Spring 2003
- Organized logistics of a clothing drive for a homeless shelter and created a Web page off the main UGBC site, advertising the drive; obtained donations from the campus; raised over 500 lbs. of clothing, which
- surpassed student government's goal by 100 lbs.
Supervised a committee of 11 students to publicize the event on campus

Advent International; Newtown, PA
Network Administration Intern   Summer 2002
- Configured, upgraded, and supported PC hardware and software in a networked environment of over 200 PC's
- Provided help desk and on site support to over 100 employees at national headquarters

Westchester Field Club; Westchester, PA
Swim Instructor, Counselor   Summer 2001
- Managed and scheduled eight swim instructors to teach basic swimming skills to a camp of 70 children, ages 5-8; designed daily learning activities to meet a variety of abilities
- Formed partnerships with three other local clubs to coordinate bi-monthly swim meets and water-polo matches

ACTIVITIES
- Information Technology Club
- Student Interviewer, Boston College Office of Admissions

SKILLS
- PC; Word, Excel, PowerPoint, Access, HTML, UNIX operating systems, JavaScript, SQL, Dreamweaver, Flash, Photoshop, Serena Collage
- Conversant in Italian

INTERESTS

- Learning new computer applications (C++), skiing, swimming

CHRIS ATTWATER
567 Rosewood Lane
Colorado Springs, CO 81207
(960) 555-1212
cattw@somedomain.com

OBJECTIVE

Executive assistant position allowing for parlay of demonstrated organization, customer service, communication and project management skills proven by 13 years of successful, profitable self-employment.

PROFILE

Motivated, personable business professional with multiple college degrees and a successful 13-year track record of profitable small business ownership. Talent for quickly mastering technology -- recently completed Microsoft Office Suite certificate course. Diplomatic and tactful with professionals and nonprofessionals at all levels. Accustomed to handling sensitive, confidential records. Demonstrated history of producing accurate, timely reports meeting stringent HMO and insurance guidelines.

Flexible and versatile -- able to maintain a sense of humor under pressure. Poised and competent with demonstrated ability to easily transcend cultural differences. Thrive in deadline-driven environments. Excellent team-building skills.

SKILLS SUMMARY

• Project Management • Report Preparation • Written Correspondence • General Office Skills	• Computer Savvy • Customer Service • Scheduling • Marketing & Sales	• Insurance Billing • Accounting/Bookkeeping • Front-Office Operations • Professional Presentations

---

PROFESSIONAL EXPERIENCE

Communication: Reports/Presentations/Technology

- Prepare complex reports for managed-care organizations and insurance companies, ensuring full compliance with agency requirements and tight deadlines.
- Author professional correspondence to customers and vendors.
- Design and deliver series of classes for local businesses and associations, providing ergonomic counseling and educating employees on proper lifting techniques to avoid injury.
- Conduct small-group sessions on meditation/relaxation techniques.
- Communicate medical concepts to patients using layman's terms to facilitate understanding.
- Rapidly learn and master varied computer programs; recently completed Microsoft Office Suite certificate course.

Customer Service/Marketing/Problem Solving

- Oversee front-office operations and provide impeccable customer service:
  --Built a clientele supported by 60% referral business.

- Develop and implement strategic marketing plan for business:
  -- Launched a thriving private practice, building revenue from $0 to over $72K in first three years with minimal overhead.
  -- Create special promotions, write/design print and outdoor advertising and coordinate all media buying.

- Won over a highly skeptical medical community as the first chiropractor to target MDs for informative in-service demonstrations, classes and booths:
  -- Presentations resulted in standing-room-only crowds of 50+.
  -- Four MDs subsequently became patients and referred family members as well.
  -- Increased client base by one-third resulting from MD referrals.

Detail Mastery & Organization

- Manage all aspects of day-to-day operations as multisite owner and practitioner of Attwater Chiropractic:
  -- Facility rental/maintenance.
  -- Patient scheduling for busy office averaging 52 appointments weekly.
  -- Finances: accounts payable/receivable, invoicing, insurance billing, budgeting.
  -- Supervision of a total of eight medical receptionist interns.
  -- Compliance with all healthcare facility, HMO and insurance requirements.

EMPLOYMENT HISTORY

ATTWATER CHIROPRACTIC -- Colorado Springs, CO; Pueblo, CO; Cheyenne, WY
Owner/Operator, 1997 to Present

LAKEVIEW RESTAURANT & CAFÉ -- Minneapolis, MN
Waitress, 1994 to 1997

EDUCATION

NORTHWESTERN COLLEGE OF CHIROPRACTIC -- Minneapolis, MN
Doctor of Chiropractic Degree, 1997

- Four-year advanced degree requiring 30-34 credit hrs. per quarter.
- GPA: 3.89/4.0
- Licensed to practice chiropractic in Colorado, Minnesota, Wyoming and Montana.

BARTON COUNTY COMMUNITY COLLEGE -- Great Bend, KS
Associate's Degree in Pre-chiropractic, 1993

- GPA: 4.0/4.0

COMPUTER SKILLS

• Microsoft Word • Microsoft Excel • Microsoft PowerPoint	• Visio • Microsoft Access • Medisoft (Insurance Billing Software)

Available for relocation
**567 Rosewood Lane | Colorado Springs, CO 81207 | (960) 555-1212 |
cattw@somedomain.com**

2.3.7 THE CURRICULUM VITAE

The primary differences between a resume and curriculum Vitae (CV) are the length, what is included and what each is used for. A resume is a one or two page summary of your skills, experience and education. While a resume is brief and concise - no more than a page or two, a curriculum vitae is a longer (at least two page) and more detailed synopsis.

A curriculum vitae includes a summary of your educational and academic backgrounds as well as teaching and research experience, publications, presentations, awards, honors, affiliations and other details. In Europe, the Middle East, Africa, or Asia, employers may expect to receive a curriculum vitae.

In the United States, a curriculum vitae is used primarily when applying for academic, education, scientific or research positions. It is also applicable when applying for fellowships or grants.

2.4 THE INTERVIEW

Before you go on your interview, you should realize there are several common types of job interviews. You will definitely want to inquire what type of job interview you will be going on beforehand so you can best prepare for it. Don't be afraid to ask your recruiter what type of job interview will be conducted, as it serves both of you and the interviewer to know.

2.4.1 SIX TYPES OF INTERVIEWS

1) Traditional one on one job interview:

The traditional one on one interview is where you are interviewed by one representative of the company, most likely the manager of the position you are applying for. Because you will be working with this person directly, if you get the job; he or she will want to get a feel for who you are and if your skills match those of the job requirements.

You may be asked questions about the experience on your resume, what you can offer to the company or position. Many times the interviewer will ask you questions such as "Why would you be good for this job?" or "Tell me about yourself." The one on one interview is by far, one of the most common types of job interviews.

2) Panel interview:

FIGURE 2.10

In a panel interview, you will be interviewed by a panel of interviewers. The panel may consist of different representatives of the company such as human resources, management, and employees. The reason why some companies conduct panel interviews is to save time or to get the collective opinion of panel regarding the candidate. Each member of the panel may be responsible for asking you questions that represent relevancy from their position.

3) Behavioral interview:

In a behavioral interview, the interviewer will ask you questions based on common situations of the job you are applying for. The logic behind the behavioral interview is that your future performance will be based on a past performance of a similar situation. You should expect questions that inquire about what you did when you were in a particular situation and how did you dealt with it. In a behavioral interview, the interviewer wants to see how you deal with certain problems and what you do to solve them.

4) Group interview:

Many times companies will conduct a group interview to quickly prescreen candidates for the job opening as well as give the candidates the chance to quickly learn about the company to see if they want to work there. Many times, a group interview will begin with a short presentation about the company. After that, they may speak to each candidate individually and ask them a few questions.

One of the most important things the employer is observing during a group interview is how you interact with the other candidates. Are you emerging as a leader or are you more likely to complete tasks that are asked of you? Neither is necessarily better than the other, it just depends on what type of personality works best for the position that needs to be filled.

5) Phone interview:

A phone interview may be for a position where the candidate is not local or for an initial prescreening call to see if they want to invite you in for an in-person interview. You may be asked typical questions or behavioral questions.

Most of the time, you will schedule an appointment for a phone interview. If the interviewer calls unexpectedly, it's ok to ask them politely to schedule an appointment. On a phone interview, make sure your call waiting is turned off, you are in a quiet room, and you are not eating, drinking or chewing gum.

6) Lunch interview:

Many times lunch interviews are conducted as a second interview. The company will invite you to lunch with additional members of the team to further get to know you and see how you fit in. This is a great time to ask any questions you may have about the company or position as well, so make sure you prepare your questions in advance.

Although you are being treated to a meal, the interview is not about the food. Don't order anything that is too expensive or messy to eat. Never take your leftovers home in a doggy bag either. You want to have your best table manners and be as neat as possible. You don't need to offer to pay, it is never expected for a candidate to pay at a lunch interview.
Chew quietly and in small bites so you don't get caught with a mouthful of food when the recruiter asks you a question.

So, now you have an idea of these six common types of job interviews. However, no matter what type of job interview you go on, always do your best to prepare for it the best you can ahead of time so you can do your best and show them the best of who you are.

2.4.2 PREPARATION FOR THE INTERVIEWING PROCESS

When you submit a job application or enquiry, you - the applicant - are in control. Normally *you* select the information to include in your resume or curriculum vita and *you* decide where to put the emphasis. There is usually time to deliberate on each individual item and the opportunity to enlist the help of friends and colleagues.

If your application is successful you may then be invited for an interview. From this point on the employer is in control. *The employer* determines the format of the interview and *the employer* sets the questions. *You* must answer the questions in real-time without consulting friends or colleagues. A great resume may get you an interview - but you need to follow-through at the interview to win the job.

Interviews divide into two categories: the screening interview and the hiring or selection interview. **Screening interviews** are used to qualify a candidate before he or she meets with a hiring authority for possible selection. The **hiring or selection interview** can take on many different forms. Screening interviews are the normal process for companies to weed out candidates for a single job opportunity. These interviews are usually quick, efficient and low cost strategies that result in a short list of qualified candidates. These interviews save time and money by eliminating unqualified candidates.

If invited to a face to face screening interview, it will usually be with a third party recruiter or someone from the Human Resources department. These are considered the gatekeepers for a company. They are typically experienced and professional interviewers who are skilled at interviewing and screening candidates. These interviewers should be effective at judging character, intelligence, and if the candidate is a good fit for the company culture. They also should be good at identifying potential red flags or problem areas in the candidate's work background and general qualifications. Some examples of screening interviews include the telephone interview, the computer interview, the videoconference interview and the structured interview.

2.4.3 PREPARING FOR THE INITIAL INTERVIEW [SCREENING INTERVIEW]

A typical hiring process consists of a screening, or initial, interview and one or more "callback" interviews. All of the strategies you used to succeed in your first interview apply to subsequent interviews—but more so. The callback interview involves more people, more time, more scrutiny and more pressure.

The initial interview screens out candidates who clearly don't have the requisite skill and fit; subsequent interviews dig deeper. At a callback interview, you are introduced to additional members of the team. This usually includes technical and or managerial members of the company. Each interviewer will have a slightly different style and perspective.

You will be evaluated on how well you fit into the firm culture and what skills, experience, and opportunities you have to offer the prospective employer. The assessment continues from the moment you arrive until you leave, many hours later, including while you are walking from one office to the next, speaking with support staff, and while at lunch. At the same time, this is your chance to determine whether the opportunity is a good fit for you, as well.

Callback interviews can take a variety of forms including meeting with a group of people at one time, dining with one or more persons, or interviewing with several individuals consecutively. Interviews with decision-makers in far-flung offices can be via videoconference or telephone. Each of these settings requires different strategies and techniques.

Those conducting first interviews often are trained in interviewing techniques. The array of people you see during subsequent meetings may include some less skilled as interviewers or who practice in an unrelated area. You may have to take the initiative to communicate what you want the interviewer to know about you and your qualifications.

Callback interviews may last from several hours to an entire day. Ask beforehand how long the interview is expected to take. It may extend longer than anticipated, so plan accordingly. Request a list of people you are expected to meet, and research their backgrounds ahead of time.

Bring several copies of your resume, transcript, writing sample, business plan, and other relevant documents– enough for everyone you are meeting and extras, in case others are added to your schedule. Be prepared to provide references shortly after your callback, if requested. You can stipulate that they not be contacted without your authorization.

Each meeting represents a fresh beginning. There is no such thing as a "rubber stamp" interview. Therefore, don't coast on the success of earlier interviews. Review your performance in the previous interview. Note any questions or situations that caused you difficulty and practice how to handle them better. Consider what made you shine, and plan to do more of the same. Take another look at the job posting, if there was one. Your responses to all questions should attempt to demonstrate that you possess the attributes the employer is seeking.

Brainstorm fresh information you can bring into a callback interview—new accomplishments, different examples, and more knowledge about the prospective employer. Keep abreast of developments relevant to the prospective employer by reviewing its website, trade publications and other sources. Consider conducting informational interviews with members of your extended network who may have valuable insights. Make a list of questions to ask your interviewers during the callback that will demonstrate your knowledge of the prospective employer's operations and challenges, and fill in any gaps in your understanding of the opportunity.

Be ready to discuss—but do not introduce—your compensation requirements and other deal points, such as willingness to travel or relocate. Do any market research necessary to prepare to negotiate if an interviewer raises the subject. The best time to discuss these topics is when the prospective employer has indicated that they are ready to make you an offer. However, you do not want to be caught unawares if they bring it up beforehand.

Moreover, you must be physically prepared to maintain focus and energy throughout the possibly lengthy callback interview. Get a good night's sleep the night before and eat a decent breakfast. Don't take the red eye and head right to your interview. If you are tired you might let your guard down or misspeak. Dress professionally but comfortably as you may be moving around their offices and walking to and from lunch. Don't wear something that will wrinkle or wilt by the end of a long day. You might want to toss a small snack into your briefcase or purse in case there is no lunch break.

Depending upon the recruiting practices of the prospective employer, their ability to schedule you with all of the appropriate interviewers, and the number of candidates under consideration, you may be asked back for several callback interviews. You also may be asked to come back for further interviews if there is some question regarding your cultural fit or skill set, or if there is a difference of opinion among the various interviewers. It is typical for finalists to be asked back one more time so that the prospective employer can evaluate all such candidates on a level playing field before a final decision is made. With some thought and advance preparation before each subsequent interview, you increase your chances of being the candidate selected to receive an offer.

2.4.4 PREPARING FOR THE ON-SITE INTERVIEW [HIRING OR SELECTION INTERVIEW]

To prepare for the on-site interview, you should know the company's products and services, financial picture, geographical locations and culture. You should take the time to find out if alumni from your institution are working there. If so, interview them about the kinds of positions that are available and the environment or workplace culture. Others in the workplace can provide firsthand knowledge about the pros and cons of working for the company. Successful interviews are those in which you, the candidate, and interviewer both leave the room with a feeling that they know and understand each other.

FIGURE 2.11

In the interview, the employer has three objectives: (1) to gather relevant information about your qualifications; (2) to assess how your qualifications match the requirements of the job; and (3) to present the organization to you in a positive way.

Your objective as a candidate should be to communicate information about yourself and your qualifications clearly and accurately, and to seek relevant information about the particular job, position, and employer.

Most interviews can be successful for you if you prepare for the expected and unexpected. This is usually a six-part process:

1. Preparation
2. Establishing rapport
3. Talking about yourself
4. Talking about the organization
5. Close-Out
6. Evaluation

You are involved in the first five segments; the sixth typically takes place while you are on site or shortly after you leave the premises.

When you travel to the interview city, you will most likely arrive the evening before the interview is scheduled. Be sure you are comfortable with knowing exactly where you are going for the interview. Plan on arriving at least 30-45 minutes before the actual interview. This allows you time to unwind, make sure that you are well groomed and have time to relax.

Most on-site interviews will put you before a panel or group, or you may be in a one-on-one setting. Be sure that your handshake is firm, and keep eye contact with each individual as you are introduced. Let the interviewer invite you to be seated. Your eye contact is very important because often it is the believability concept that sells what you are saying. Your body language also sends a message of confidence and sincerity. In addition to the firm handshake and eye contact, be sure to have well-balanced posture, an open, relaxed facial expression, a firm voice, and use appropriate gestures when emphasizing key words.

The first 30 seconds to five minutes of the interview are very important. The first impression is next to impossible to change. You never get a second chance to make a first impression. Your appearance and dress are critical in that you should fit into the culture of the workplace by dressing appropriately. You should wear conservative colors and avoid excessive jewelry, flashy colors, excessive makeup, strong perfumes or colognes.

Be sure that you have practiced your 30 second or 3-5 minute infomercial. The strong lead tells the interviewer about yourself, what your assets and strengths are and the value you can bring to their organization. Be prepared to give examples of a time when you exemplified leadership, a time when things were not going well and you turned them around. Also be prepared to discuss your involvement in professional societies, civic organizations and summer or part-time employment. Be able to describe a time when you experienced failure and the lessons that came from that experience.

Be yourself during the interview. Bear in mind that the organization chose to interview you. Let the knowledge and your interview preparation bolsters your confidence. During the interview, take notes. Inform the interviewer(s) at the beginning of the interview that you would like to take some notes to help in the questioning and answering session at the end of the interview.

The competencies that will be evaluated during the interview are skills that you have polished during your education, extracurricular involvement, internships, co-op and summer experiences. The areas that will be evaluated are adaptability, communication, initiative, interpersonal acumen, planning and organization, accountability, resourcefulness, work orientation, and negotiation skills among others. Be a good listener but not reticent about asking penetrating questions.

Some routine questions that will be asked of you during the interview are listed below:

- Tell me about yourself. What do you look for in a job? What are your special abilities? How do you perform under pressure?
- Why did you choose your particular field of study and work? What do you perceive as the advantages of your chosen field?
- What makes you think that you could be successful with our organization? What do you know about our organization?
- What types of positions are you most interested in?
- Are you willing to relocate multiple times?
- What have you learned from some of the jobs that you have held?
- Is your GPA indicative of your ability?
- What leadership positions have you held in college and in your community?
- Are you very creative? Give some examples.
- What is your philosophy of management?
- Why should we hire you?

In answering all questions, be specific, concise, and give examples that show your ability to provide direction, allocate resources, that you can execute with quality, and have a passion to succeed. Exemplify that your value system is one of fairness, truth telling, promise keeping, and respect for all individuals.

Be prepared for the unexpected by writing down five questions that you hope no one would ever ask you in the interview. Take some time and thoughtfully answer those questions. Once you master how you would answer those questions on site, your comfort level will come naturally.

Some routine questions that you may want to ask the interviewer are:

- If hired, would I be filling a newly created position, or would I be replacing someone?
- Would you describe a typical work day and the things that I would be responsible for and accountable for?
- What are the most critical duties of the job?
- How will I get feedback on my performance?
- What is the career path from this position to the top of the organization?
- How does this position contribute to the bottom line of the organization?
- What is the diversity mix of your management, the organization and the area in which you will be working?

Do not ask about salary. Let the organization bring up the subject.

During the interview, sell yourself, show what you can do for the organization, show that you are a team player, ask for the job, and never apologize for any areas where you need growth. Present those areas from a positive viewpoint if they must be discussed. Project confidence and never imply that you can work miracles. You should not discuss religion, politics or race, although, as stated above, you may ask about the company's diversity.

Be sure that you never lose your personal touch, and give the interviewer(s) a true sense of the value that you can bring to their organization by letting your unique qualities come out.

Consult a dining etiquette book or website to be sure that you are prepared in case part of the interview takes place in a restaurant or company dining room.

Be clear, as you end the day, on what the next steps in the process are for moving forward. If an offer is made on the spot, thank the organization and take some time to ponder in order to make an informed decision. Send a personal handwritten thank-you note to those who interviewed you in the process.

It is important that you feel valued, challenged, and have an excellent compensation package, training for personal and professional development, and clearly defined career progression.

2.4.5 PREPARING FOR VIDEO CONFERENCE, COMPUTER AND PHONE INTERVIEWS

As companies continue to look for ways to trim costs, video, computer and telephone conferences are quickly becoming an initial first step for interviewing non-local candidates. The telephone interview is the most common way to perform an initial screening interview. This helps the interviewer and the candidate get a general sense if they are mutually interested in pursuing a discussion beyond the first interview. This type of interviewing also saves time and money. They may be tape recorded for the review of other interviewers. The goal, for the candidate during the phone interview, is to arrange a face to face meeting.

To prepare for a telephone interview:

- Minimize distracting background noise prior to the call's start. Barking dogs, television noise and flushing toilets can blow it.
- If the call is unexpected, ask to reschedule for a time when you'll have had a chance to prepare yourself and your environment.
- If the interview is scheduled, keep your résumé and notes close for reference.
- Like a video interview, avoid checking your blackberry or e-mail, and pay close attention to the conversation. Phone interviewers judge candidates by what they say and how they say it. Lulls in conversation can indicate a lack of focus or knowledge on a subject.

FIGURE 2.12

Therefore a few additional preparation tips should be kept in mind for phone interviews:

- Turn call-waiting off so your call isn't interrupted.

- Clear the room of other people and pets. Turn off the stereo, TV and close the door.

- Keep your resume in clear view, on the top of your desk, so it's at your fingertips when you need to answer questions.

- Don't eat or drink during the interview.

- Smile, as it will change the tone of your voice.

- Speak slowly and enunciate clearly.

- Don't interrupt the interviewer.

- Take your time - it's perfectly acceptable to take a moment or two to collect your thoughts.

- Give concise answers.

The computer interview involves answering a series of multiple-choice questions for a potential job interview or simply for the submission of a resume. Some of these interviews are done through the telephone or by accessing a web site. One type is done with pushing the appropriate buttons on the telephone for the answer you are submitting. Wal-Mart uses this method for screening cashiers, stockers, and customer service representatives.

Another type of **computer interview** is provided by **accessing a website** while using a computer keyboard and a mouse. Lowes Home Improvement uses this type of screening. Some of the questions on both of these types of interviews are related to ethics. As an example, "If you see a fellow co-worker take a candy bar and eat it, do you a. Confront co-worker, b. Tell the supervisor, c. Do nothing."

Face-to-face interviews are the preferred selection tool for recruiters, but this may be changing as videoconference technology becomes more available and easy to use. It doesn't hurt that videoconference interviews take up less resources in terms of people, time, money, and environmental impact. They allow companies to broaden their applicant pool in a world that's becoming more globally competitive. More than half of the largest U.S. companies do videoconference interviews. The Modern Language Association (MLA) has increased their use of videoconference interviews from 12% to 18%, and any college career center worth its salt includes tips and advice on preparing for a videoconference interview. Chapman and Webster in 2003 anticipated that 10% of companies would be hiring purely from videoconference interviews.

Videophone and Video Conferencing interviews provide the transfer of audio and video between remote sites. More than half of the largest U.S. companies already utilize videoconferencing. It is a convenient communication method and an alternative to the more costly face-to-face meetings. Anyone, anywhere in the world can perform videoconferencing with the use of a microphone, camera and compatible software. Videoconferencing is available on the Internet. Its continual drop in cost is making it a popular resource for businesses as well as for home use.

Although telephone interviews save a lot of money and resources in the recruitment process, few companies are rash enough to actually hire someone based on phone interviews. There's something about needing to "see it in order to believe it." For better or for worse, nonverbal cues such as eye contact, smiling, body orientation, gestures all influence a person's perception and ability to trust in another person, which you can't get over the phone.

For those of you who are concerned about how applicants perceive videoconference interviews. An informal poll on Microsoft's Job Blog reported that 88% of poll participants preferred videoconference to telephone interviews. In an early 1997 study by Kroeck and Magnusen, a remarkable 54% of applicants rated videoconference interviews the same or preferable to a traditional face-to-face interview. While applicants have a harder time reading how a videoconference interview went, applicants definitely feel they are better able monitor themselves, respond to questions, and know their interviewer(s). Of course, it's also good to take into consider the impression a phone or videoconference interview may give about your company, after all, not everyone is a videoconference fan.

Here are several tips on how to prepare for your video interview:

- Dress as you would for a face-to-face interview - from head to toe. Even though the camera may catch you from waist-up at your desk, don't take the chance being viewed in shorts.
- Try to maintain eye contact with remote viewers and avoid frequently looking away, which could create an impression that you're distracted.
- DON'T CHECK YOUR BLACKBERRY.
- Speak clearly and pay close attention to the interviewer's conversation with you, even if the interview is being simultaneously broadcast to multiple offices.

- When emphasizing something important, lean in slightly toward the camera. If you're a small person in a large chair, sit on the edge of your seat to maintain a strong visual presence.

Take Away Points:

- videoconference interviews can be used not only to screen applicants but to hire applicants
- applicants like being able to see and respond to interviewers although they have a harder time knowing if they did well on an interview
- technical problems will probably come up–how an organization handles technical problems rather than detract from the experience can reveal what a group is really like
- if you're at home, remember to lock up your dog before going into the interview–oh, and don't sneeze or make fast hand movements

FIGURE 2.13

Tips for a successful videoconference interview:

Appearance:

- Pastel shirts and interesting ties that are not too busy in pattern are best. Pastel shades work well
- on television, as do bright blues, pinks, fuchsia and green.

- Avoid large areas of red, bright whites, black and navy, as well as plaid, stripes and overly busy
- patterns.

- High gloss lips and glittery jewelry will catch the light and be distracting.

Body Language:

- Look straight into the monitor at the interviewer. It will give the impression that you are looking into their eyes.

- Most people find that it only takes a few minutes to get comfortable in a videoconference interview. Focus on the person you are talking to and soon you will forget the camera is running. Avoid excessive motion. Rocking in your chair or rapid arm movements will appear as a blur to the other person. Don't be unnaturally stiff however. Relax just as you would if you were speaking to someone in person.

- Speak naturally. The microphones will pick up your audio without you having to raise your voice. There is no need to shout.

- Show your energy and enthusiasm. Remember that the camera will stay static. Image and voices are all you have to make yourself interesting and stand out. Don't forget to smile!

Set-up:

- Arrive at the videoconference site early enough to get comfortable with the equipment. You want to make sure that everything is working properly and that the table, chair, and microphone are set up to your advantage. Position yourself so that you are looking into the camera, not at the monitor, to give the impression of eye contact. Have the camera as close to eye level as possible so that you are not looking up or down at the interviewers. It is best to position the camera and the monitor so that you can glance at the other participants in the monitor briefly, without breaking your gaze at the camera too often.

- Center yourself in the screen and at a medium distance rather than at the end of a long conference table. You should appear from about the middle of your upper arms and have an excess of screen space above your head. Sit up straight; do not slouch or lean to the side. Leaning forward slightly towards the camera helps increase eye contact. Conversely, leaning back can create a feeling of distance.

- Set up your notes, pen, water, and reading glasses so that they are accessible but out of camera range. Remember to refrain from shuffling papers or tapping a pen during the interview, however, as that will be picked up on the microphone.

- If possible, arrange the lighting so that you are not in unflattering shadows or washed out, and your coloring is as lifelike as possible. Watch for reflection from your glasses. Don't forget, however, that the camera catches everything while it is on. Therefore, do not use it as a mirror to fix your hair or makeup before the interview. Likewise, do not relax or comment inappropriately after the interview until you are sure the camera is off.

Etiquette:

- Hesitate slightly: Be prepared for a very slight delay in receiving the audio and video. This takes a few moments to get used to. Try and get into the habit of hesitating slightly before speaking to assure that the other person has finished speaking, and again when you complete what you have to say so that other participants know that you are done

- Speak clearly and listen carefully.

- Each participant in the videoconference should introduce themselves, and state their location if there are various offices involved, at the beginning of the interview or anytime a new participant joins the session. Jot down this information so you can use your interviewers' names during the interview, and address your questions and comments as appropriate.

- Videoconference interviews also differ from in-person meetings in that there is no opportunity for a handshake to begin or end the session. Therefore, to wrap things up, summarize your main points, thank the interviewers for their time, let them know you are interested in the job, and ask about next steps. Pay attention to the time without obviously glancing at your watch and follow the interviewer's cues that the session is drawing to a close.

- Rehearse: A dry run with a friend is critical for you to have an idea of what to do and where to look as well as any potential hiccups.

For both telephone and video conference interviews, it helps to practice. You can practice in the mirror or even by recording yourself. Additionally, it's nice to send a follow-up thank you that reiterates your top selling points. Be sure to proofread, though.

2.4.6 DEADLY MISTAKES MADE IN JOB INTERVIEWS

There are three main reasons why interviews may go wrong:

a) You can't articulate yourself and communicate exactly why you are the perfect fit for the job.

b) You are unprepared; you can't give the right answer to the tough question behavioral questions.

c) You are too nervous; you can't control your nerves and unfortunately lose control during the interview.

Since no two interviews are alike, it is difficult to be prepared for what lies ahead, but you can focus on your presentation skills, which may be even more important than what you have to say. Three areas of performance, which should be considered dangerous and deadly, are worth spending some time thinking about before your next interview.

1. Poor Non-verbal Communication Image

It's about demonstrating confidence.

- Stand straight, and make good eye contact.
- Connect with a good, firm handshake.
- Sit erect and lean forward in the chair, appearing interested and attentive.

That first impression can be a great beginning, or a quick ending to your interview.

2. Poor Verbal Communication Skills

Your interviewer is giving you information, either directly or indirectly.

- Good communication skills include listening and letting the person know you heard what they said.

- Observe your interviewer's style and pace and match that style, adjusting your style and pace to match.

- Use appropriate language. Beware of using slang words or references to age, race, religion, politics, or sexual preferences, these topics could get the door slammed very quickly.

- Telling the interviewer more than they need to know could be a fatal mistake. Too much information, particularly personal information, could get into some areas that are best not discussed in an interview.

3. Not Asking Questions

It is extremely important to ask questions.

- When asked, "Do you have any questions?" if you answer "No," it is the WRONG answer!

- Asking questions gives you the opportunity to show your interest. The best questions come from listening to what is said and asked during the interview. Ask for additional information.

- Asking questions gives you the opportunity to find out if this is the right place for you. Your interview is your chance to find out what goes on in the company.

The job market is very competitive and the competition is fierce. Give yourself every advantage by preparing and practicing before the interview. Be aware of your verbal and non-verbal performance and the messages you are sending. It could make the difference between a job offer or not.

2.4.7 THE TONE OF YOUR VOICE DURING INTERVIEW

Often, your **tone of voice** says more than your words do. You can say that you know how to perform the job duties, but if it doesn't sound like you do, you won't inspire much confidence in the hiring manager. In addition, avoid saying anything offensive or vulgar! (Absolutely no swear words/cussing!) Avoid using any of the following words or phrases:

Bling	Hater	Jacked Up	Nerd
Beast	Shorty	Like	Props
Bomb (Da Bomb)	Snap (Oh Snap)	Ill	Yo
Bro	Trick (Trick Out)	Word	Sucks
Busted	Yeah Right	Sup	Sweet
Chill (Chill Out)	Whatever	Tight	OMG
Dawg	Salty	Score	Sick
Dude	Homie	Head	Juiced
Fiending	Hook (Off the Hook)	Hell	Emo
Frontin	Bum	Bogus	Crispy
Geek	Duh	Freak Out	Blitz
Ghetto	Cool	Crunk	Cop Out
Hick	Fed Up	Bounce	Fly
My bad	As If	Ballin	Chick

How to SOUND MORE CONFIDENT during the job interview:

☑ Pause before answering to give yourself time to gather your thoughts. A five second pause may seem like a long time to you, but it will likely show the interviewer that you have considered your answer.

☑ Stick with a factual but interested tone. Avoid raising the pitch of your voice at the end of a statement. Doing so can change the tone of your statement to one of a question, which makes you seem uncertain. Avoid using the same tone for every answer, though, as it can make you sound bored.

☑ Practice your answers before you go. If you have a good answer prepared and practiced, it will be on the tip of your tongue! You will sound more confident if you are not trying to think up an answer on the spot.

☑ Try to eliminate or reduce the number of times you say *um, uh, like,* and *you know.* These filler phrases imply that you are not sure about what you want to say.

☑ Don't use "weak words." Starting your answers with *I think that I am...*and *I hope to...*and *I believe that I can...*imply that you are not certain of your abilities.

☑ Don't apologize for being nervous. Doing so actually calls more attention to the fact that you are worried about your performance.

☑ You can get public speaking practice before the interview by joining a local public speaking group, such as Toastmasters (http://www.toastmasters.org).

Figure 2.14

2.4.8 TOUGH JOB INTERVIEW QUESTIONS

This section contains twenty of the toughest interview questions with sample answers.

1. How would you describe yourself?

Sample excellent response:

My background to date has been centered around preparing myself to become the very best financial consultant I can become. Let me tell you specifically how I've prepared myself. I am an undergraduate student in finance and accounting at _____ University. My past experiences have been in retail and higher education. Both aspects have prepared me well for this career.

2. What specific goals, including those related to your occupation, have you established for your life?

Sample excellent response 1:

I want to be working for an excellent company like yours in a job in which I am managing information. I plan to contribute my leadership, interpersonal, and technical skills. My long-range career goal is to be the best information systems technician I can be for the company I work for.

Sample excellent response 2:

My goals include becoming a Certified Financial Advisor so I can obtain a better working knowledge of financial research analysis. That background would enable me contribute to my client base as a better financial consultant since I would have that extra insight into the companies they seek to invest in. I could then be a portfolio manager or even branch office manager.

3. How has your college experience prepared you for a business career?

Sample excellent response:

I have prepared myself to transition into the work force through real-world experience involving travel abroad, internship, and entrepreneurial opportunities. While interning with a private organization in Ecuador, I developed a 15-page marketing plan composed in Spanish that recommended more effective ways the company could promote its services. I also traveled abroad on two other occasions in which I researched the indigenous culture of the Mayan Indians in Todos Santos, Guatemala, and participated in a total-language-immersion program in Costa Rica. As you can see from my academic, extracurricular, and experiential background, I have unconditionally committed myself to success as a marketing professional.

4. Please describe the ideal job for you following graduation.

Sample excellent response (equates ideal job with job he's interviewing for):

My ideal job is one that incorporates both my education and practical work skills to be the best I can be. Namely combining my education in finance with my working knowledge of customer-service operations, entrepreneurial abilities, computer skills, and administrative skills. I want to utilize my analytical expertise to help people meet their financial goals. This is exactly why I am convinced that I would be a very valuable member of the Merrill Lynch team.

5. What influenced you to choose this career?

Sample excellent response:

My past experiences have shown me that I enjoy facing and overcoming the challenge of making a sale. Without a doubt, once I have practiced my presentation and prepared myself for objections, I feel very confident approaching people I don't know and convincing them that they need my product. Lastly, I like sales because my potential for success is limited only by how much of myself I dedicate toward my goal. If any profession is founded on self-determinism, it surely must be sales.

6. What will it take to attain your goals, and what steps have you taken toward attaining them?

Sample excellent response:

I've already done some research on other workers at Merrill Edge to see how they achieved similar goals. I know that Merrill Edge encourages the pursuit of a graduate degree and will reimburse for tuition. I plan to pursue an MBA to give me an even more extensive knowledge of business and financial analysis.

7. How do you determine or evaluate success? Give me an example of one of your successful accomplishments.

Sample excellent response:

Last semester I was hired by my university's Council for Student Activities. The group negotiates contracts of entertainers, sets up sound equipment, markets the entertainers to students, and generally decides what kind of programming should be done. When I got hired, I didn't know the first thing about how fill any of those responsibilities. I decided, however, that I wasn't going to fail. Four months later, I have become the Webmaster for the group. I also write our campus newsletter and created Game Night, a student competition of table games. That event yielded the biggest audience ever for a non-concert event.

8. Explain why you have, above all others applying for this position, the qualifications and personal characteristics necessary for success in this position?

Sample excellent response:

I believe I have a combination of qualities to be successful in this career. First, I have a strong interest, backed by a solid, well-rounded, state-of-the-art education, especially in a career that is technically oriented. This basic ingredient, backed by love of learning, problem-solving skills, well-rounded interests, determination to succeed and excel, strong communication skills, and the ability to work hard, are the most important qualities that will help me succeed in this career. To succeed, you also need a natural curiosity about how systems work -- the kind of curiosity I demonstrated when I upgraded my two computers recently. Technology is constantly changing, so you must a fast learner just to keep up, or you will be overwhelmed. All of these traits combine to create a solid team member in the ever-changing field of information systems. I am convinced that I possess these characteristics and am ready to be a successful team member for your firm.

9. Are you more energized by working with data or by collaborating with other individuals?

Sample excellent response:

I like the validity of information and also like the energy that comes with working with people. The best thing about working in a group is combining the great minds from different perspectives and coming up with something extremely great, compared with when you're working alone. At the same time, information can generate vitality in the project you're working on. No matter how many heads you've got together, without information, you can't go very far. The perfect situation would be a combination of working with information and people, and I'm confident of my abilities in both areas.

10. By providing examples, convince me that you can adapt to a wide variety of people, situations and environments.

Sample excellent response:

I've shown my ability to adapt by successfully working in several very different jobs. For example, I lived with a native family in Costa Rica. I worked as a nanny for a famous writer in Cape Cod. I was responsible for dealing with Drug Court participants. And I catered to elite country-club clientele. I did it all well and had no trouble adapting.

11. Describe a time when you were faced with problems or stresses that tested your coping skills.

Sample excellent response:

Arriving at the language school I was attending in Costa Rica in the middle of the night with very minimal Spanish-language skills, I found my way to a very small town with no street addresses or names and found my temporary residence. I was scared, but I handled the situation very well, very calmly. In very stressful situations, I am always the one in the group to stay calm and focused. My friends, family, and professors have always said that I am an oasis of calm in a storm.

12. Give an example of how you applied knowledge from previous coursework to a project in another class.

Sample excellent response:

Last semester I was taking a microeconomics and a statistics course. One of the microeconomics projects dealt with showing the relationship between the probability that customers would stop buying a product if the price was raised a certain amount. Through what I learned in statistics I could find the median where the price was the highest and still kept most of the customers happy.

13. Describe an instance when you had to think on your feet to extricate yourself from a difficult situation.

Sample excellent response:

When I was a resident assistant at my college, a student I did not know asked me if he could use my phone to call another room. Although I did not know the student, I allowed him into my room. He used the phone and in the course of this conversation, he stated that he had just come from a fraternity party and was high from taking some drugs. Well after his conversation, I had to enforce the student conduct code by writing him up. He became very hostile toward me and would not give me any identification or information. I stood in the doorway to prevent him from leaving. I noted the serial numbers on his keys, so when the situation got to the point where I felt unsafe, I allowed him to leave. I still preformed my job without jeopardizing my or his physical welfare.

14. Describe a situation in which you were able to use persuasion to successfully convince someone to see things your way?

Sample excellent response:

Recently my company asked for bids on a phone system for our new college campus. Two companies came in very close with their bids, and most of my department wanted to go with a vendor that we have used in the past. After I looked over the proposals, it was clear that this was the wrong decision. So, I talked individually with each member of our staff and succeeded in changing their minds and get the best product that would save money and provide the highest quality.

15. Tell me about the salary range you're seeking.

Sample excellent response 1:

I am sure that I am the candidate you are looking for. If you feel the same, then I'm sure your offer will be fair and commensurate with the value I can bring the company.

Sample excellent response 2:

I am not depending on money to make me happy. What makes me happy is having a satisfying job that provides challenge and new situations daily.

Sample excellent response 3:

A salary commensurate with my experience and skills is important, but it's only one piece of the package. Many other elements go into making up a compensation package, but more importantly, it's critical to me to enjoy what I'm doing, fit into the corporate culture, and feel I'm making a genuine contribution.

16. Do you have a geographic preference?

Sample excellent response:

Although I would prefer to stay in the Mid-Atlantic area, I would not rule out other possibilities.

17. Would it be a problem for you to relocate?

Sample excellent response:

I'm open to opportunities within the company; if those opportunities involve relocation, I would certainly consider it.

18. Tell me what you know about our company.

Sample excellent response:

You're large and respected worldwide. You're both a clinical and teaching hospital. Over the last 60 to 70 years you've produced award-winning research. In reviewing your Web site, I've familiarized myself with many of your corporate goals and objectives.

19. Why did you decide to seek a position in this company?

Sample excellent response:

I am convinced that there would be no better place to work than Accenture. You are the top consulting firm in the United States. You provide your employees with the tools they need to stay competitive and sharpen their skills while working in an open, team-based environment. I am also aware that you provide a mentor for all new employees, and I would embrace any opportunity to work with a mentor and eventually become one myself.

20. What personal weakness has caused you the greatest difficulty in school or on a job?
Sample excellent response (shows how he recognized his weakness and worked to improve):
My greatest weakness used to be delegation. To improve my workers' efficiency, I would take it upon myself to do many small projects throughout my shift as a manager that could have been done by others. Once I realized that I was doing more work than the other assistant managers, and they were achieving better results, I reevaluated what I was doing. I quickly realized that if I assigned each person just one small project at the beginning of the shift, clearly state expectations for the project, and then follow up, everything would get done, and I could manage much more efficiently and actually accomplish much more.

2.5 SUMMER INTERNSHIP & CO-OP EXPERIENCE

Internships are usually, but not always, one term. Internships are usually, but not always, in summer. Co-ops are usually, but not always, multi-term; e.g. you might work fall semester, go to school in spring semester, work summer, go to school in fall, and work the next spring semester. Schedules vary depending on when you need to be in school and when the employer needs you to work

Internships can be either part-time or full-time; depends on employers' needs and the way each employer chooses to structure an intern program. Some internship programs are very formal and structured, while others offer more flexibility to negotiate terms. Co-ops are always full-time positions.

Internships can be paid or unpaid; this depends on employers' preferences and on the career field and on the job market supply and demand conditions which exist. Co-op positions are always paid.

The compensation for co-op and internship positions varies greatly among employers and geographic locations. You will have to do a salary research for salaries in your field. Be aware that in some career fields, unpaid internships are common and are the best way to get career-related experience.

Most institutions consider an "internship" just a summer job, with no academic credit earned. However, for internships and co-ops, the authority to grant academic credit is entirely determined by each academic department; that is, some absolutely never do, some commonly do; with some it might be negotiable. Ask in the department of your academic major. If your department allows this, academic credit is usually earned by registering for a Field Study or something similar, and usually requires you to submit academic work, such as reports, to a faculty member, in addition to the employer's on-the-job requirements. Some departments offer internship seminars or courses, in which they assist you with internships. Again, this is entirely up to the individual academic department.

Internships are not always in the summer. You will find the majority of internships offered in summer, but some employers offer internships year 'round, including fall semester or spring semester terms. Some employers (such as tax preparers or political campaigns) may have a busy season during the year when they employ interns — and therefore offer non-summer internships.

If you work only in the summer, this is typically referred to as an internship (although some employers may call this a co-op). However, some employers do not offer summer-only programs. Be aware of the requirements of each employer as you search for your job.

If you intend to do an internship during the Fall or Spring semester then first check with your academic department (the department which offers your major) to find out what affect leaving campus for a semester will have on your academic standing and your ability to get the courses you need in the appropriate sequence. If you are receiving scholarships or financial aid, inquire in those offices what affect leaving campus for a semester will have on your scholarship or financial aid. Determine whether or not you need to be formally enrolled as a student during your internship to meet the employer's requirements or for other reasons. If so, inquire about your academic department's policy to see if it offers or allows (or requires) academic credit for an internship. Only academic departments may grant academic credit.

You can search for a job in a particular location, but you are advised to look at all opportunities. You should be aware of the job market for your skills and take that into consideration — some career fields offer more opportunity and you may be able to be more selective about location. Other career fields are more competitive and you may need to go where the employers have needs. Some employers may assist with relocation and living expenses.

Only a very few employers provide housing; some rent-free; some require you to pay rent. Some employers provide assistance finding housing. Some provide some financial assistance or allowance for moving and/or housing. If you get a job offer and the employer hasn't explained exactly what help they provide, you should ask.

No student is guaranteed an internship or co-op job. Applying for a co-op or internship position is competitive. Employers evaluate your resume and compare you to your peers at your institution and possibly at other institutions.

For summer internships, start in fall and keeping looking through spring — until you get a position. Use school breaks (Thanksgiving, winter & spring breaks) to make contacts at home, if "home" is where you would like to be located for your internship. For co-op positions, begin looking at least one semester before you hope to begin work. Be aware that if an employer requires a security clearance, it may take up to six months between the time the employer begins considering you and the time you can begin work.

Benefits of hiring co-op students:

- Provides an excellent pool of well-prepared employees.
- Improves personnel selection process by using actual on-the-job performance as a basis for permanent hiring decisions.
- Increases cost-effectiveness of recruitment and training. Studies show employers save money by using co-op to identify and train personnel.
- Improves workforce diversity through access to minority students for permanent employment.
- Increases retention rates among permanent employees recruited and hired through a co-op program. Both students and employers have the time to try out the position and ensure that the fit is the most productive and effective for both.
- Enhances human resource flexibility with effective short-term employees.
- Strengthens company relations with colleges and students. Through evaluations, advisory boards and other means, employers can work with colleges to ensure an effective curriculum.

Employers' responsibilities of the co-op student:

- Provide the student with paid, challenging work experience in an area specifically related to the student's academic field of study.
- In multiple co-op assignments, the work should be progressive in nature.
- Evaluate the co-op student twice during the co-op assignment with the forms provided by Career Services at the institution (at mid-point and at the end of the assignment), and return them to Career Services in a timely manner.
- Read the student's completed technical report and sign the required statement on the first page, verifying the report does not contain proprietary material and may be forwarded on to the appropriate academic department at the institution for grading.

The basic requirements of most co-op programs:

1. Endorsement and support of the supervisor and management. It is crucial that management be actively supportive of a co-op program to 1) ensure participation from their employees; 2) acknowledge the co-op's credibility and 3) make sure the co-op is not being relegated solely to "back-burner" projects.
2. Active and supportive mentor at the company. Whether the supervisor also plays a role as mentor, or another person is asked to take on this part, the mentor is essential in the real-life development of the student's abilities, work habits and interpersonal skills.
3. The co-op benefits from active mentor interaction in the following areas:

- Learning by experience
- Improving self-confidence
- Getting career advice
- Gaining a sense of value to the company
- Learning the ropes of the company (culture, values, presentation skills, where power lies, etc.)
- Experiencing the day-to-day management process

4. Strong communication between the supervisor and co-op.
5. Successful supervisors:
   - Take a strong interest and concern in developing the co-op
   - Have a broad base understanding of the industry and organization
   - Getting career advice
   - Have relevant areas of expertise
   - Are easily accessible to the co-op
   - Offer mutual respect
   - Teach and encourage the co-op
   - Evaluate the co-op fairly and honestly
   - Provide constructive suggestions for improvement.
6. Appropriate training/orientation. To ensure a smooth transition period for co-op students and the company, an orientation session in the company is very helpful.
7. Acquaint the co-op with the work site, company expectations, and areas of responsibility.

The Career Services at most institutions offers numerous options for recruiting students for internships and co-op positions. Their services range from on-campus interviews, mock interviews and job fairs, to video conferencing and general job postings.

CHAPTER 3
Student Success

CHAPTER 3
STUDENT SUCCESS

6.1 WHAT IS STUDENT SUCCESS?

Students' persistence to completion of their educational goals is a key gauge of student success and therefore institutional success. Two most frequently cited statistics in connections with student success are the freshman-to-sophomore retention rate, or first-year annual return rate and the cohort graduation rate. The freshman-to-sophomore retention rate measures the percentage of first-time, full-time students enrolled at the university the following fall semester. The cohort graduation rate is defined as the percentage of an entering class that graduates within three years with an associate's degree, and within four, five, or six years with a baccalaureate degree. Since the annual return rate of students as they progress through a program is directly related to their degree/certificate completion, the concept of retention usually includes year-by-year retention or persistence rates as well as graduation rates. Together, these statistics represent student success. These student success statistics are commonly regarded as primary indicators of institutional performance. They have come to reflect the overall quality of student learning and intellectual involvement; how well integrated students are in campus life; and how effectively a campus delivers what students expect and need.

Student success is beneficial to society because students:

- understand the rights and responsibilities that allow them to function as contributing members of our democracy.

- cooperate and collaborate with others in work, social, and family settings.

- make independent decisions based on reasoning and supported by facts.

- relate in a positive and constructive manner with family members and other members of the world community.

- take responsibility for their own actions and act supportively and compassionately toward others.

6.2 DESIRABLE OUTCOMES OF STUDENT SUCCESS

The following desirable outcomes have been the most frequently cited indicators of student success in higher education.

Student Retention: Entering college students remain, re-enroll, and continue their undergraduate education. Alternatively, student retention is an institutional goal of keeping students enrolled for consecutive semesters until degree completion. (For example, first-year students return for their sophomore year.)

Student Persistence: individual goal of a student reaching his or her *specific educational attainment*.

Educational Attainment: entering students persist to completion and attainment of their degree, program, or educational goal. (For example, 2-year college students persist to completion of the associate degree, and 4-year college students persist to completion of the baccalaureate degree).

Academic Achievement: students achieve satisfactory or superior levels of academic performance as they progress through and complete their college experience. (For example, students avoid academic probation or qualify for academic honors.)

Student Advancement: students proceed to and succeed at subsequent educational and occupational endeavors for which their college degree or program was designed to prepare them. (For example, 2-year college students continue their education at a 4-year college, or 4-year college students are accepted at graduate schools or enter gainful careers after completing their baccalaureate degree.)

Holistic Development: students develop as "whole persons" as they progress through and complete their college experience. This outcome consists of multiple dimensions, which may be defined or described as follows:

- *Intellectual* Development: developing skills for acquiring and communicating knowledge, learning how to learn, and how to think deeply.

- *Emotional* Development: developing skills for understanding, controlling, and expressing emotions.

- *Social* Development: enhancing the quality and depth of interpersonal relationships, leadership skills and civic engagement.

- *Ethical* Development: formulating a clear value system that guides life choices and demonstrates personal character.

- *Physical* Development: acquiring and applying knowledge about the human body to prevent disease, maintain wellness, and promote peak performance.

- *Spiritual* Development: appreciating the search for personal meaning, the purpose of human existence and questions that transcend the material or physical world.

Colleges and universities retain students, while students persist to a goal. The assumption underlying retention is *retention to degree from original institution*. Individual students' goals are different from institutions' goals. A student may successfully persist to his or her individual goal(s) without being retained to graduation. "Educational attainment" captures the variability of students' goals and disentangles retention and persistence.

6.3 SEVEN CENTRAL PRINCIPLES OF STUDENT SUCCESS

The critical first step toward promoting student success is to define it, i.e., to identify positive student outcomes that represent concrete indicators of student success. Step two is to identify the key, research-based principles or processes that are most likely to promote student success and lead to positive student outcomes. Serendipitously, the same success-promoting principles serve to promote three key student outcomes simultaneously: a) student retention / persistence, b) student learning (academic achievement), and c) personal development (holistic outcomes). This serendipity supports the long-held contention among student retention scholars that "successful retention is nothing more than successful education"

The following seven processes are offered as the most potent principles of student success because they are well supported by higher education scholarship and are firmly grounded in research and theory:

1. personal validation
2. self-efficacy
3. sense of purpose
4. active involvement
5. reflective thinking
6. social integration
7. self-awareness

6.3.1 PERSONEL VALIDATION

Student success is more likely to be realized when students feel personally *significant*—i.e., when they feel *welcomed*, recognized as *individuals*, and that they *matter* to the institution. In contrast, student success is sabotaged by college practices or policies that depersonalize or marginalize students. Students are more likely to become committed to the institution and, therefore stay, when they come to understand that the institution is committed to them. Programs cannot replace the absence of high quality, caring and concerned faculty and staff.

6.3.2 SELF-EFFICACY

Student success is more likely to take place when students believe that their individual effort matters, i.e., when they believe they can exert significant influence or control over their academic and personal success. Conversely, the likelihood of student success is reduced when students feel hopeless or helpless. Meta-analysis research indicates that academic self-efficacy is the best predictor for student retention and academic achievement. Personal traits such as self-efficacy, self-esteem, and internal locus of control are among the best predictors of job performance and job satisfaction.

6.3.3 SENSE OF PURPOSE

Student success is more probable when students find meaning or purpose in their college experience—i.e., when they perceive relevant connections between what they're learning in college and their current life or future goals. In contrast, lack of personal goals for the college experience and perceived irrelevance of the college curriculum are major causes of student attrition.

When students are provided with a personally relevant context for a new concept, they continue to think about that concept longer than if they learn it without reference to a personally relevant context and the more relevant the academic content is to students, the more likely they are to engage in higher-level thinking with respect to it.

6.3.4 ACTIVE INVOLVEMENT

The probability of student success increases commensurately with the degree or depth of student engagement in the learning process, i.e., the amount of time and energy that students invest in the college experience—both inside and outside the classroom. In contrast, student persistence and academic achievement is sabotaged by student passivity and disengagement.

The greater the student's involvement or engagement in academic work or in the academic experience of college, the greater his or her level of knowledge acquisition and general cognitive development. Research also indicates that student involvement outside the classroom is a potent predictor of student retention. For instance, students who utilize such support services, and interact with the professionals involved with the provision of such services, are more likely to persist to college completion.

6.3.5 REFLECTIVE THINKING

Students are more likely to experience success when they engage in reflective thinking about what they are learning and elaborate on it, transforming it into a form that relates to what they already know or have previously experienced. Successful learning requires not only action, but also reflection. Such reflection or thoughtful review is the flip side of active involvement. Brain research also shows that active involvement and reflective thinking involve two distinct mental states of consciousness, the former characterized by faster, low-amplitude brain waves and the latter by slower, higher-amplitude brain waves. Both mental processes are needed for learning to be complete. Active involvement is necessary for engaging student attention—which enables learners to initially get information into the brain, and reflection is necessary for consolidation—keeping that information in the brain, by locking it into long-term memory.

6.3.6 SOCIAL INTEGRATION

Student success is enhanced by human interaction, collaboration, and formation of interpersonal connections between the student and other members of the college community—peers, faculty, staff, and administrators. In contrast, feelings of isolation or alienation are likely to contribute to student attrition. Students who have become "socially integrated" or "connected" with other members of the college or university are much more likely to complete their first-year of college and continue on to complete their college degree. The importance of social integration and interpersonal interaction for learning is also supported by the epistemological theory of social constructivism; according to this theory, human thinking is shaped by social interaction and conversation, whereas an individual's thought process is largely an internalization of these external dialogues.

6.3.7 SELF AWARENESS

Student success is promoted when students gain greater awareness of their own thinking, learning styles, and learning habits, i.e., when they engage in meta-cognition—when they think about their thinking, when they self-monitor or check their comprehension, and when they self-regulate or accommodate their learning strategies to meet the demands of the learning task at hand. Research demonstrates that high-achieving college students tend to reflect on their thought processes during learning and are aware of the cognitive strategies they use. Successful college students also "self-monitor" their academic performance, that is, they maintain awareness of whether or not they are actually learning what they are attempting to learn and they self-regulate or adjust their learning strategies in a way that best meets the specific demands of the subject matter they are trying to learn. Lastly, self-awareness has been found to be a critical element of any effective self-management and self-improvement plan whether it is the management of time, money, or health.

6.4 FACTORS THAT INFLUENCE STUDENTS' SUCCESS IN COLLEGE

Although academic success means that a student has fulfilled the requirements for his course of study, more goes into doing well in college than just concentrating on grades. Although academic factors account for 68 percent of success in school, other things influence a student's academic success as well. Students who fully prepare for their upcoming tasks and who tap into the resources in their environment stand the best chance of doing well in college.

FIGURE 6.1

Family Influences

A student's family exerts a large influence on how well he or she does in school. Having parents and siblings who concern themselves with the student's academic well-being gives him or her necessary support to handle the stress of college. Additionally, the family should have realistic expectations of how university life will affect the student. It's not unusual for parents to receive frequent texts and emails about homesickness and other difficulties. Knowing about some of these eventualities helps the family and the student cope with school, particularly if he or she is a first-generation student.

The Student's Role

College students' success rests just as much on themselves as it does on the support of their family. Students with good self-discipline, emotional self-control and academic self-confidence stand the best chance of moving successfully into college life. These qualities allow students to involve themselves in the academic environment without becoming overwhelmed by the obstacles that arise from it.

Aside from these intangible factors, a strong GPA in high school often represents the most accurate indicator of students' future success. If they didn't keep up on grades, attend class regularly and develop solid study habits in high school, their chances of succeeding at college are hampered considerably.

Academic Goals

College students' goals work in tandem with factors such as grades and self-discipline in determining how well they'll meet the challenges of college. Once students decide what their goals are, research suggests that they make friends with similarly minded people. Friends who have incompatible goals can knock a student off course. For example, a student serious about academic success who has very social, party-oriented friends may find it difficult to keep up a high GPA if he or she frequently attends social events.

On-Campus Help

An academic advisor can help guide students toward college success if they meet with the advisor regularly. This on-campus resource helps students stay on track by explaining the particulars of their degree and what classes they need to meet the academic requirements of their major. The advisor also provides the student with a more realistic understanding of how much work is required to succeed in college. They may offer pointers about seeking help from professors and other on-campus resources and amenities.

6.5 ADJUSTING TO COLLEGE

Attending college is one of the first major life transitions for many young adults. Some students are excited to take on the new experiences of campus life, while others feel apprehensive about making this change. Regardless of your outlook when beginning your first year of college, you may benefit from talking with others who have already made that transition.

Making the Transition

What are some of the most common changes you can expect in the first year on campus?

- **New environment and relationships.** First year students must adapt to an unfamiliar environment, adjust to different living arrangements, and develop new relationships. Living with roommates may be the first 'test' freshmen experience. Students face the challenge of adjusting to roommates who may have very different boundaries and individual needs than family and friends from home. Roommates may or may not develop close friendships, but communication and compromise can build a smoother transition. College brings a unique opportunity to interact and live with students from various backgrounds and cultures. Expanding your worldview by learning about each other's differences and similarities will likely enhance your college experience.

- **Greater personal freedom.** Living on your own for the first time means that you will gain independence and take charge of the many choices and decisions that your parents and teachers made for you in the past. While this new found freedom can be exciting, it may also feel overwhelming and less predictable than what you are accustomed to. The freedom to manage your daily life is a learning process, but one that can be very satisfying.

- **Added responsibility.** First-year students must manage the important daily responsibilities that accompany their increased personal freedom. Students must manage basic tasks such as eating, sleeping, exercising, and going to class. New students must also address more complex responsibilities such as balancing studying and socializing, participating in clubs and activities, and handling finances. Managing time is a demand that all first-year students experience. A typical day in college is less structured than high school, and there is more reading and studying that is required outside of class. Some students may feel as if they have no free time to do anything but schoolwork, while others feel like they have too much free time outside of the classroom.

- **Changing relationships.** While there are many changes occurring in your new campus life, there will also be changes in your relationships. New students often face challenges such as best friends going to other universities, beginning new romantic relationships or maintaining existing ones, and juggling newly formed relationships with already established ones. Students must balance a sense of connectedness and separation while at college. Some freshmen feel the need to call or e-mail home several times a week in the first few months away, while others require less frequent communication with their family and friends.

Common Stressors

The first year of college is a new and exciting adventure, but one that may come with a few challenges along the way. Below are most common stressors that first-year students experience.

- **Time Management.** Now that you are in college, there are no more eight hour school days like those in many high schools. You may have class for six, three, or even zero hours a day. The rest of your time must be negotiated between homework, clubs and activities, work, socializing, and self-care. College students often feel as if there is just not enough time to do everything that needs to be done. Using a schedule and some organizational skills will help you to effectively manage your hectic and changing life.

- **Academic Performance.** By nature, college coursework is challenging, and it can be hard to keep up with the increased academic demands. Some students undergo pressure from both themselves and their parents. There may be requirements for scholarships and graduate school admission that you have not previously experienced. In order to manage the increased demands and expectations, it is important to attend class regularly, keep up with readings and assignments, and ask for help when you need it. Professors and teaching assistants are there to assist you, and want you to succeed. If you need additional help, various organizations on campus offer tutoring services, many of which are free.

- **Roommate Conflict.** Learning to live with someone new can be one of the most challenging aspects of going to college. Different living habits are the most common source of roommate conflict (i.e. neat vs. messy; quiet vs. noisy; early-to-bed vs. up-all-night). Failure to communicate your expectations about living together can lead to tension and eventually conflict. To avoid "roommate fallout" you should communicate your needs and expectations respectfully, while recognizing your own habits and quirks that might affect your relationship. If conflict does escalate you should take it to a Resident Advisor, Resident Director, or a Counselor to determine a course of action.

- **Long Distance Dating Relationships.** It is not uncommon for first-year students to begin college in a long distance dating relationship. Where at one time this relationship may have helped you cope with everyday stress, it could now be a source of distress due to the distance between you and your partner. Uncertainty in what the future holds for the relationship is one of the most common stressors experienced by college students in long distance dating relationships. There are a few key efforts that each partner can make to lessen the sting of separation. Verbal communication, openness, and assurance of one another can reduce stress associated with being separated. It is also essential for each partner to seek social support from others and remain active in their individual lives while apart.

- **Body Image.** Many college students also struggle with body image. Our culture pays a great deal of attention to the appearance of our bodies, particularly during young adulthood. Media representations of the ideal body, messages from peers, and other cultural factors shape what we perceive as "normal" or "good". It can be difficult to have a clear, healthy perspective on ourselves and our bodies when our culture sends so many confusing, conflicting, and sometimes unhealthy messages. This can be stressful at a time when many are trying to "fit in" with others and make new, exciting relationships. If you find yourself preoccupied with how you look or become distressed about your body, discussing your concerns and ideas with someone can be extremely helpful in creating, developing, and maintaining a body image that is healthful and fulfilling.

Recommendations for First-Year College Students

What steps can you take to have a great first year of college?

- **Be patient.** While campus may seem new and overwhelming for new students, it becomes more familiar with time. Refer to the many resources available to assist you in navigating your surroundings. Maps, your Resident Advisor (R.A.), upper-classman, and the university Websites are all useful tools to get you through the initial transition to campus.

- **Connect with other students.** If you talk to other students, you are likely to discover that they share similar questions and concerns. Your R.A. is an excellent person to go to when issues arise. She or he is equipped to help you solve problems and refer you to appropriate resources.

- **Get involved.** Student organizations are a fun way to interact with other students and faculty. Meeting people with similar interests and goals is an exciting way to make friends and participate in social activities.

- **Utilize resources.** There are numerous resources on campus designed to create a rewarding college experience. In addition there are numerous sources of support such as the Office of Dean of Students, the Counseling Center, the Career Center, your Academic Advisor, financial aid programs, and mentoring/tutoring programs offered to address various student needs. Some colleges and universities have cultural programs such as (Lesbian, Gay, Bisexual, Transgender, Queer/Questioning) LGBTQ to assist the diverse campus's needs.

- **Care for yourself.** The foundation for a productive college career is a healthy lifestyle. Take the necessary steps for nurturance, getting adequate rest, socializing, and physical activity. Campus Recreation offers several resources that students can utilize to work towards wellness. The Anti-Virus Research Center (ARC), Continuing Respiratory Care Education (CRCE), and the Wellness Center are just a few campus facilities that strive to promote healthy practices and to educate the campus community on various health topics.

6.6 STUDENT TIME MANAGEMENT

Student time management is one of the most important skills for students to manage their study and get good grades.

The following scenarios are a good indication of poor time management:

1. feel stressed and overwhelmed by a lack of time.

2. are studying at hours when you are not fresh and productive.

3. procrastinating on that must-do homework.

4. cramming the night before.

5. not getting assignments in on time.

The demands of school, work, and social life can mean that you leave things to the night before or forget to hand in that important assignment. Good time management helps you juggle your busy life. The next five sections offer advice to help students manage their time better in college.

6.6.1 GET A HELICOPTER VIEW OF YOUR SCHEDULE

As a student, one of the first things you want to do is to get an academic planner. An academic plan highlights any bottle necks of intense periods of assignments and assessments. This lets you know when 'all hands should be on deck.'

In your academic planner put:

- Assignment due dates and other assessment due
- Exam dates
- Social functions that need to attend, such as a family birthday or regular sporting events.

6.6.2 CREATE A MASTER TO-DO LIST

Student life can be overwhelming! With assignments to hand in, assessments to complete, and exams to sit, it is easy to feel overwhelmed and stressed.

One of the best things that you can do is to list all the things that you need to do.

The very act of writing things down and getting them out of your head and onto paper reduces your stress and gives you a clear idea of what you need to do.

Make sure that some of your master to-do list is aligned with your specific goals as a student.

6.6.3 USE A WEEKLY PLAN

By planning your work and then working your plan, you avoid the trap of last minute cramming sessions and stressful write-ups of assignments the night before.

An efficient use of time management will help students to reduce stress, increase the quality of studying and will improve your grades. But the benefits extend beyond college and study as time management is a transferable skill that is valued by employers. The best way to set up a short-term time management plan is to develop a weekly plan that reflects the natural ebb-and-flow of most people's short-term horizons.

Using a student planner tool of your work and then working your plan is essential for student success. Good planning involves identifying what is important to you and then protecting your time for those things.

6.6.4 WORK YOUR PLAN

One of the biggest problems for students is not the plan; it is putting the plan into action.

Some of the common barriers to student time management are:

1. Procrastination. Facebook...Internet...even washing the dirty dishes - all have been used as a form of procrastination when there is a need to do some study. One research study quoted that 80% of students procrastinate on important assignments and study.

2. Lack of focus. Everywhere you look there are distractions....Facebook, TV, surfing the Net. All of this can mean that you spend less time focusing on school work.

3. Poor prioritization. With too much to do and not enough time you are going to have prioritize your work. Keep a daily time management to-do-list to prioritize your work like a professional.

Whether you are:

- an elite athlete,
- a top business professional or
- a great student,

.....any success started with small steps and then building on those successes.

6.6.5 IMPROVE YOUR STUDY TECHNIQUES

Studying effectively is not an all-night cram session the day before the exam. Nor is it chaining yourself to a desk for 12 hours straight. Being a student involves readings, attending lectures and tutorials, and participating throughout the semester. One important student time management tip is being able to plan and manage the new information. This involves keeping up-to-date with readings and being an active contributor to your learning experience. One part of academic performance is being able to connect and relate facts with larger patterns of knowledge, and then communicating them in your own words.

6.6.6 TIME MANAGEMENT COLLEGE ACTIVITY: BIG ROCK LITTLE ROCK STORY

The 'Big Rocks Little Rocks' story starts with a professor who stands in front of a class holding a glass jar, into which he places a number of large rocks.

FIGURE 6.2

After filling the jar with large rocks the professor asks the students, "Is the jar full yet?"

Most of the class replied, "Yes!"

Then he reaches into his pocket and pulls out a number of smaller rocks and puts them into jar with the big rocks.

After which he says, "Is the jar full yet?"

Still many in the class reply "Yes!"

From the other pocket the professor pulls out a bag of sand and proceeds to fill the glass jar.

The sand fills the gaps between the big and small rocks.

Again he asks, "Is the jar full yet?"

Some of the class replies guardedly, "Yes it's now full."

The professor now produces a glass of water and proceeds to pour the water into the jar. The water seeps into the sand and finally fills the jar.

What is the moral of the story?" the professor asks.

One girl replied "That no matter how full the jar, you can always fit more into it".

However the professor shook his head. "No No No…"

"The moral of the story" said the professor, "is that you need to get the big rocks of your day or life out of the way first or all the other small stuff will get in the way and take up space"

If the professor had first filled his jar with sand and small rocks then he never would be able to put the big rocks into the jar.

This story highlights that it is important to get the big rocks of your life, those high impact activities, into the jar before the smaller stuff crowds it out. Are you getting your big rocks done at college and in your life? To know what your big rocks are you need to be able to figure out what it is about college life that you want. What is important to you? Do you want good grades? Are you a student who believes that anything higher than a pass is wasted effort? Are you a student who wants to genuinely learn his or her art and good grades is just a by-product? In essence - what drives you as a student?

By having a vision of what you want to achieve, whether it is good grades or a dream job, knowing how you will achieve your vision is the essence of student goal setting. Student goal setting keeps you motivated, gives you confidence, and helps you to persist when the last thing you want to do is to sit at the desk and study.

6.5 STRATEGIES FOR STUDENT RECRUITMENT AND SUCCESS

Recruitment Strategies

Common strategies for recruitment include community outreach, high school outreach, financial aid, and climate and inclusion for undergraduates and graduate student recruitment for graduate students. Figure 6.3 shows an estimator or profile for predicting the likelihood of students who will graduate from two- or four institutions.

Community Outreach

- Promote programs which bring residents from the surrounding communities to campus. Pay attention to community outreach, with particular emphasis on underrepresented populations.

- Create a multicultural recruitment day to bring under-represented groups to introduce students to the University.

- Recruit community college students and other transfer students. A sizeable number of underrepresented and low-income students are enrolled at community colleges. Forming partnerships with these institutions is a strategy for recruiting underrepresented students.

- Recruit and develop cooperative programs with institutions that enroll large numbers of students from racial and ethnic minority groups (e.g. HBCU's).

- Collaborate with pre-college programs and high schools to identify prospective recruits.

High School Outreach

- Host workshops and orientations for middle and high school students. College Prep Day for middle and high school students that includes workshops, student panels, campus tours, and information about application process. Host a Minority Scholars Weekend or a three day orientation for high school students to stay in residence halls and attend classes.

- Visit racially diverse high schools and college fairs where diverse students are represented.

- Enhance bridge programs to develop a smooth pipeline from K-12 to college, with particular emphasis on underrepresented groups. These programs must include components that reach out to potential students, families of potential students, guidance counselors, K-12 school administrators, and community organizations. The intent is to better inform and better prepare potential students for pursuing a college education.

- Offer summer programs that expose high school students to science, engineering, technology, and mathematics.

- Monitor the participation of students enrolled in institutionally-sponsored pre-college programs.

- Include guidance counselors from high schools in the area, especially those from racially and ethnically diverse high schools, in a campus orientation.

- Fund support programs for area schools.

Financial Aid

- Provide advising and outreach about financial aid opportunities to low-income and other underrepresented groups.

- Support University development efforts that prioritize resources for need and merit-based financial aid.

Climate and Inclusion

- Involve currently enrolled students, faculty, and staff in recruitment initiatives.

    1) Multicultural Student Recruitment Committees: Faculty and staff join committee to aid the Admissions in staying connected to multicultural communities and suggesting recruitment ideas for those communities.

    2) Multicultural Student Receptions to introduce newly admitted minority students to the campus community and expose the students and their families to multicultural student organizations, student support services and alumni of the University.

- Personalized the recruitment of underrepresented students.

    1) Parent-to-Parent Letter: Letter from the parent of a currently enrolled minority student to the parents of admitted students. The letter discusses the transition to college and the great opportunities that their child and the family have participated in and how much they love the college or university.

- Disseminate information about campus diversity to prospective students and their families.

    1) Create a Diversity website to direct prospective students to resources and support.

    2) Send multicultural newsletters to all admitted students.

    3) Develop foreign language websites of key information for the admission process and university information.

- Ensure that images and messages in publications, office buildings, webpages, etc. indicate a welcoming environment.

Graduate Student Recruitment

- Recruit at graduate school fairs and conferences.

- Establish relationships with faculty at other institutions to facilitate referral of potential graduate students.

- Host campus visits and information sessions for prospective graduate students.

- Encourage underrepresented undergraduate students to pursue graduate education.

- Develop baccalaureate to master's transition enhancement programs.

- Create opportunities for participation in undergraduate research with efforts to encourage participation of underrepresented students.

- Establish mentoring programs for advising and supporting graduate students.

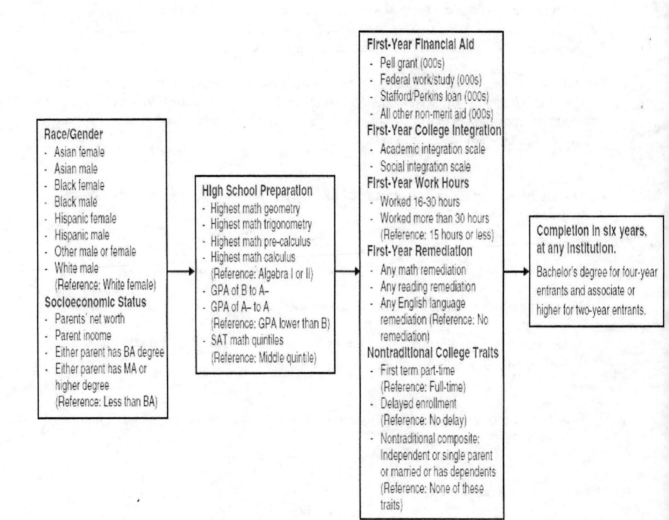

FIGURE 6.3

6.6 MODELING STUDENT SUCCESS [RETENTION & PROGRESSION]

The following seven variables can be used to model retention and progression. They are:

1) Learner characteristics
2) Learner behaviors
3) Academic integration
4) Social-psychological integration
5) Other learner support
6) Course/program characteristics
7) Instructor behaviors

Figure 6.4 is a black diagram of the seven variables

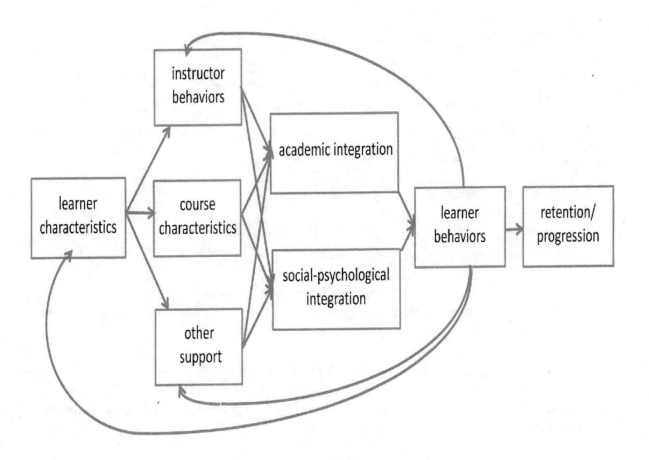

FIGURE 6.4

Table 6.1 is a matrix for modeling retention and progression. Example 6.1 is a sample matrix for modeling student success.

TABLE 6.1

PREDICTOR CATEGORY *italics* = research literature regular = partner experience **bold**=PAR Framework findings —limited list of predictors below each category—	CONNECTION application to enrollment (advising to enrollment)	ENTRY completion of gatekeeper courses (beginning of class)	PROGRESS entry into program to 75% of classes complete (middle of class)	COMPLETION of course of study & credential w/ market va (end of class)
LEARNER CHARACTERISTICS *prior GPA; achievement beliefs; content Knowledge & skills; ...* **1st time in college**				
LEARNER BEHAVIORS attendance/log ins; *participation in orientation programs; withdrawals;...engagement*				
ACADEMIC INTEGRATION *participation in student learning communities; peer mentoring;...specialized program coordinators*				
SOCIAL/PSYCHOLOGICAL INTEGRATION *perceived social presence; participation in freshmen interest groups;...specialized program coordinators*				
OTHER LEARNER SUPPORT *ongoing student support services...*				
COURSE/PROGRAM CHARACTERISTICS *perceived interactivity; ...perceived utility*				
INSTRUCTOR BEHAVIORS/CHARACTERISTICS *faculty responsiveness;...perceived social presence*				

Targeted Focus [T] • General Focus [G]

"In a national sample, approximately 59% of Bachelor of Arts recipients graduated from a different college than the first institution they attended" (National Center for Education Statistics [NCES], 2003).

Implication: Institutions will fail to "retain" students most of the time.

Interventions targeted toward the following items will have the greatest numerical potential for improving completion rates:

•*preventing* delayed entry to college
•*increasing* part-timers' level of enrollment
•*boosting* financial aid in colleges
•*reducing* students' work hours

Example 6.1

Interpret what particular groups of students who can be targeted with this student success model.

PREDICTORS *italics* = research literature regular = partner experience **bold = POC findings**	CONNECTION application to enrollment (advising to enrollment)	ENTRY completion of gatekeeper courses (beginning of class)	PROGRESS entry into program to 75% of requirements complete (middle of class)	COMPLETION of course of study & credential w/ market value (end of class)
learner characteristics *prior GPA(1)* *self-motivation(2) . . .* *attitudes towards tech (10)* *content knowledge & skills (11)* **being net new/no prior college** **Need Dev-Ed/Take DevEd** **#prior courses with C or better**	New Student Orientation (UIS)	Services for students with disabilities (UIS) Technology Helpdesk (UIS) Tutoring (UIS) Referrals to Counseling (UIS)	Services for students with disabilities (UIS) Technology Helpdesk (UIS) Tutoring (UIS) Referrals to Counseling (UIS)	Services for students with disabilities (UIS)
learner behaviors *easy access to a computer (13)* *participation in tutorials (14) . . .* **too many concurrent courses**		Tutoring (UIS) Referrals to Counseling (UIS)	Tutoring (UIS) Referrals to Counseling (UIS)	
academic integration *participation in tutorials (14)* *peer mentoring (17)* *student learning communities (20)* *orientation programs (21)* *freshman interest groups (22)* *program coordinators (24)*	Online program coordinators (UIS)	Online program coordinators (UIS) Writing center (UIS) Social media groups (UIS) Honors Program (UIS) Work study (UIS)	Online program coordinators (UIS) Writing center (, UIS) Social media groups (UIS) Honors Program (UIS) Work study (UIS)	Online program coordinators (UIS)
social/psychological integration . . .	Online program coordinators (UIS)	Online program coordinators (UIS)	Online program coordinators (UIS)	Online program coordinators (UIS)
other learner support . . .	Financial Aid (UIS)	Financial Aid (UIS)	Financial Aid (UIS)	
course/program characteristics . . .		QM reviews for some classes (UIS)	QM reviews for some classes (UIS)	
instructor characteristics/ behaviors *perceived social presence (15)* *perceived interactivity (16) . . .*		Community of Practice for E-Learning (UIS) Center for Online Learning Research & Service Fellows (UIS)	Community of Practice for E-Learning (UIS) Center for Online Learning Research & Service Fellows (UIS)	

general focus – institution wide   targeted focus – targets particular groups of students or programs

6.7 SHARED RESPONSIBILITY

First and foremost all people associated with the college or university show be attentive on student success. All administrators, support staff, and faculty should know the university or college and know its students. Student success should be everyone's business. Mission statements and institutional leadership should focus on student success.

Universities and colleges should specify the path to student success. Draw an accurate map; 'distribute' it widely and follow it consistently. Implement a comprehensive network of early warning systems and safety nets. If something works, consider requiring it. Conduct ongoing outcomes assessment and use the results. Do more of what you know works for student success; do less of what you know doesn't work or can't demonstrate that it does. Review and revise time commitments and priorities. Align the reward system with the institutional mission, values, and priorities. Invest in student learning and activities that contribute to student success. Invest in faculty and staff members who are doing the right things. Make every student residence a learning community. Build and renovate spaces to reflect commitment to student engagement.

Appendices

HOMEWORK FOR CHAPTER 1

1. Which age in the history of technology was the chariot discovered?

2. Spectacles were created during which age in the history of technology?

3. Which age in the history of technology was the fountain pen discovered?

4. During which decade the first integrated circuit for commercial use was created?

5. What was the disadvantage of vinyl records during the 1970s?

6. What company built the first computer suitable for use in elementary school classrooms?

7. What is Artificial Intelligence (AI)? What impact did Artificial Intelligence had in the 1980s?

8. What is the full definition of the internet?

9. What was the Y2K bug? How was it fixed?

10. What advantage does the Digital Versatile Disc (DVD) have over the Compact Disc (CD)?

11. As of 2009, smartphones have become very popular. Why?

12. What are the difference among a scientist, engineer, technologist and technician?

13. Which professional of Question 12 would likely be concerned with just theory?

14. Which professional of Question 12 would likely be concerned with just applications?

15. Which two professionals of Question 12 it would be argumentative in determining how much theory and applications would be used in their careers?

16 Who would use more theory, the engineer or the technologist?

17. What is the difference between engineering technology and technology?

18. Which type of Information Technology (IT) specialist would provide technical assistance and advice to an individual who just purchased a new type of software?

19. Describe one of the top ten emerging environmental technologies.

20. How did the graphic communication industry started?

21. Which type of technologist in the graphic communication industry is considered a visual communicator?

22. Describe the subtle yet important divergence of electronics engineering from electrical engineering?

23. What are the most popular career options for a technologist in chemicals?

24. What does a medical technologist career involves?

25. Which branch of engineering or engineering technology are involved with human characteristics & performance?

HOMEWORK FOR CHAPTER 2

1. What are some unfortunate circumstances that can lead to a violation of ethics in the workplace?

2. What are some possible resolutions to maintaining ethics?

3. What are the five principles of a morally good person?

4. List some inner strength realistic goals that can help prevent an employee from violating ethics?

5. List some outer strength realistic goals that can help prevent an employee from violating ethics?

6. What is the definition of ethics?

7. Would a person who avoids stealing from a store only because it has a surveillance camera be considered an ethical person?

8. Who should you consult if you are faced with an ethical dilemma on your job?

9. Describe the two types of sexual harassment that can occur in the workforce?

10. What are the four key categories of attributes that will help you to maintain and nurture your repudiation?

11. Why is it is very difficult to obtain a software patent compared to a software copyright?

12. What is the purpose of a cover letter?

13. What three paragraphs should be included in your cover letter?

14. How far back should "years of experience" go on your resume?

15. What is the recommend font and font size for a hard copy of your cover letter and resume?

16. What is the purpose of the thank-you letter after your interview? How should this letter be sent?

17. What are the items to include on a letter acknowledging a job offer?

18. What does accepting a job offer ethically obligates you to?

19. What is the definition of a resume?

20. What should you do if you rather work for General Electric Company, but Westinghouse Electric Corporation has given you a great offer, and you don't want to turn that down if General Electric Company doesn't want you?

21. What are the two categories of interviewing?

22. How do you prepare for a telephone interview?

23. How do you prepare for a video interview?

24. What are the benefits of hiring co-op students?

25. What are the employers' responsibilities of the co-op student?

HOMEWORK FOR CHAPTER 6

1. What are the major attributes of a good laboratory student?

2. You are performing an experiment with two others. You are reading the meter scale, Kenjoseph is varying the voltage and Demora is taking data. Who is responsible for recording the data correctly?

3. Classify the following errors as gross (G), systematic (S), or random (R). In some cases more than one classification applies. Hint: Use the internet to research more about each case.

Type of Error	*Classification (G, S, or R)*
a. meter incorrectly zeroed	G, S
b. not following approved procedure	_____
c. oscilloscope attenuator controls not dented (locked into) in the cal mode	_____
d. micrometer caliper not zeroed	_____
e. sloppiness in an instrument's adjustment	_____
f. drafts	_____
g. friction	_____
h. friction in inclined-plane experiment where lubricant and other variables are constant	_____
i. reading a meter scale from the side (always the same side)	_____
j. dirt in a balance scale pivot	_____
k. failure to level a surface plate	_____

13. What recommendations for first-year college students are offered, according to the textbook?

14. List the three most important items to put into an academic planner?

15. Write a weekly plan for all your courses for this month.

16. Discuss the three common barriers to student time management.

17. Describe the common strategies for college recruitment.

18. Name the seven variables used to model retention and progression.

19. *Institutions will fail to "retain" students most of the time.* Pick an American college or university and do research to report the percentage of students who graduated from the "original" school they attended.

20. Describe the four interventions to retaining students.

21. Within the university infrastructure who is responsible for student success.

APPENDIX B

CONVERSION FACTORS

Time

1 day = 1.44×10^3 min = 8.64×10^4 s
1 year = 8.76×10^3 h = 5.26×10^5 min = 31.5×10^7 s
1 h = 60 min = 3600 s
1 min = 60 s

Displacement (Length)

1 meter (m) = 100 cm = 1000 mm = 39.4 in = 3.28 ft
1 centimeter (cm) = 10 millimeters (mm) = 0.394 in
1 kilometer (km) = 10^3 m = 0.621 mi = 3280.8 ft
1 foot (ft) = 12 in = 0.305 m = 30.5 cm
1 inch (in) = 0.0833 ft = 2.54 cm = 0.0254 m = 25.4 mm
1 mile (mi) = 5280 ft = 1.61 km = 1760 yd
1 yd = 3 ft = 36 in = 0.9144 m
1 revolution = 360° = 2π rad

Area

$1 \text{ m}^2 = 10^4 \text{ cm}^2 = 1.55 \times 10^3 \text{ in}^2 = 10.76 \text{ ft}^2$
$1 \text{ cm}^2 = 10^{-4} \text{ m}^2 = 0.155 \text{ in}^2 = 100 \text{ mm}^2$
$1 \text{ ft}^2 = 144 \text{ in}^2 = 9.29 \times 10^{-2} \text{ m}^2 = 929 \text{ cm}^2$
$1 \text{ yd}^2 = 9 \text{ ft}^2$
$1 \text{ ft}^2 = 144 \text{ in}^2$

Volume

$1 \text{ m}^3 = 10^3 \text{ liters (L)} = 10^6 \text{ cm}^3 = 35.3 \text{ ft}^3 = 6.10 \times 10^4 \text{ in}^3$
$1 \text{ ft}^3 = 1728 \text{ in}^3 = 2.83 \times 10^{-2} \text{ m}^3 = 28.3 \text{ L}$

Velocity (Speed)

1 m/s = 3.28 ft/s = 2.24 mi/h = 3.60 km/h
1 ft/s = 0.305 m/s = 0.682 mi/h = 1.10 km/h
60 mi/h = 88 ft/s
1 km/h = 0.278 m/s = 0.913 ft/s = 0.621 mi/h
1 mi/h = 1.47 ft/s = 0.447 m/s = 1.61 km/h
1 rpm = 0.10472 rad/s
60 rpm = 1 cps = 1 Hz

Mass

1 kilo-gram (kg) = 10^3 grams (g) = 0.0685 slug
1 kg = 2.2 pounds (lb) = 2.2046 lbm
1 slug = 14.6 kg
1 slug = 32.2 lb
1 g = 1000 mg

Force

1 newton (N) = 0.225 lb = 3.60 ounces (oz)
1 pound (lb) = 16 oz = 4.45 N
1 lb = 0.454 kg = 454 g

Pressure

1 pascal (pa) = 1 N/m^2 = 2.09×10^{-2} lb/ft^2 = 1.45×10^{-4} lb/in^2
1 lb/in^2 = 144 lb/ft^2 = 6.90×10^3 N/m^2
1 atmosphere (atm) = 1.013×10^5 N/m^2 = 14.7 lb/in^2
1 kPa = 20.89 lb/ft^2

Work (Energy, Torque)

1 joule (J) = 0.738 ft-lb = 2.39×10^{-4} kcal = 0.0009485 Btu = 6.24×10^{18} eV
1 foot-pound (ft-lb) = 1.36 J = 1.29×10^{-3} Btu = 3.25×10^{-4} kcal
1 kilocalorie (kcal) = 4185 J = 3.97 Btu = 3077 ft-lb
1 Btu = 0.252 kcal = 778 ft-lb = 1054.8 J
1 kilowatthour (kWh) = 3.6×10^6 J = 3.6 MJ = 2.655×10^6 ft-lb

Power

1 watt (W) = 1 J/s = $0.738 \dfrac{\text{ft - lb}}{\text{s}}$ = 0.001341 hp
1 kilowatt (kW) = 10^3 W = 1.34 hp

1 horsepower (hp) = $550 \dfrac{\text{ft - lb}}{\text{s}}$ = 745.7 W = $33,000 \dfrac{\text{ft - lb}}{\text{min}}$

Temperature

$$T_C = \frac{5}{9}\left(T_F - 32°\right)$$

$$T_F = \frac{9}{5}\left(T_C + 32°\right)$$

APPENDIX C

METRIC OR SI PRE-FIX CHART

Prefix	Symbol	Value
Tera-	T	10^{12}
Giga-	G	10^{9}
Mega-	M	10^{6}
Kilo-	k	10^{3}
Hecto-	h	10^{2}
Deka-	da	10^{1}
Base Unit	--------	$10^{0} = 1$
Deci-	d	10^{-1}
Centi-	c	10^{-2}
Milli-	m	10^{-3}
Micro-	μ	10^{-6}
Nano-	n	10^{-9}
Pico-	p	10^{-12}

APPENDIX D

MATHEMATICAL REFERENCE TABLES
ENGLISH-METRIC EQUIVALENTS

LENGTH MEASURE

1 inch (in) = 25.4 millimeters (mm)
1 inch (in) = 2.54 centimeters (cm)
1 foot (ft) = 0.3048 meter (m)
1 foot (ft) = 12 inches (in)
1 yard (yd) = 3 feet (ft)
1 yard (yd) = 36 inches (in)
1 yard (yd) = 0.9144 meter (m)
1 mile (mi) = 1.609 kilometers (km)
1 millimeter (mm) = 0.03937 inch (in)
1 centimeters (cm) = 0.39370 inch (in)
1 meter (m) = 3.28084 feet (ft)
1 meter (m) = 1.093 61 yards (yd)
1 kilometer (km) = 0.62137 mile (mi)

1 rod = $16\frac{1}{2}$ feet (ft)

1 rod = $5\frac{1}{2}$ yards (yd)

1 statute mile = 5,280 yards (yd)

AREA MEASURE

1 square inch (in^2) = 645.16 square millimeters (mm^2)
1 square inch (in^2) = 6.4516 square centimeters (cm^2)
1 square foot (ft^2) = 0.092903 square meters (m^2)
1 square foot (ft^2) = 144 square inches (in^2)
1 square yard (yd^2) = 0.836127 square meters (m^2)
1 square yard (yd^2) = 9 square feet (ft^2)
1 square millimeter (mm^2) = 0.001550 square inches (in^2)
1 square millimeter (mm^2) = 0.000001 square meter (m^2)
1 square centimeter (cm^2) = 0.15500 square inches (in^2)
1 square centimeter (cm2) = 0.0001 square meters (m^2)
1 square decimeter (dm^2) = 0.01 square meter (m^2)
1 square dekameter (dam^2) = 100 square meters (m^2)
1 square hectometer (hm^2) = 10,000 square meters (m^2)
1 square meter (m^2) = 10.763910 square feet (ft^2)

1 square meter (m^2) = 1.19599 square yards (yd^2)
1 square kilometer (km^2) = 1,000,000 square meters (m^2)
1 square rod = 30.25 square feet (ft^2)
1 acre = 160 square rods
1 acre = 4,840 square yards (yd^2)
1 acre = 43,560 square feet (ft^2)
1 square mile = 640 acres

VOLUME MEASURE FOR SOLIDS

1 cubic inch (in^3) = 16.387064 (cm^3)
1 cubic foot (ft^3) = 0.028317 (m^3)
1 cubic foot (ft^3) = 1,728 cubic inches (in^3)
1 cubic yard (yd^3) = 0.764555 (m^3)
1 cubic yard (yd^3) = 27 cubic feet (ft^3)
1 cubic centimeter (cm^3) = 0.061024 cubic inches (in^3)
1 cubic centimeter (cm^3) = 0.000001 cubic meters (m^3)
1 cubic millimeter (mm^3) = 0.000000001 cubic meters (m^3)
1 cubic meter (m^3) = 35.314667 cubic feet (ft^3)
1 cubic meter (m^3) = 1.307951 cubic yards (yd^3)
1 cubic decimeter (dm^3) = 0.001 cubic meter (m^3)

VOLUME MEASURE FOR FLUIDS

1 gallon (gal) = 3,785.411 cubic centimeters (cm^3)
1 gallon (gal) = 3.785411 liters (L)
1 quart (qt) = 0.946353 liters (L)
1 ounce (oz) = 29.573530 cubic centimeters (cm^3)
1 cubic centimeter (cm^3) = 0.000264 gallon (gal)
1 liter (L) = 0.264172 gallon (gal)
1 liter (L) = 1.056688 quarts (qt)
1 cubic centimeter (cm^3) = 0.033814 ounces (oz)

MASS MEASURE

1 pound (lb) = 0.453592 kilogram (kg)
1 pound (lb) = 453.592 grams (g)
1 ounce (oz) = 28.349523 grams (g)
1 ounce (oz) = 0.028350 kilogram (kg)
1 kilogram (kg) = 2.204623 pounds (lb)
1 gram (g) = 0.002205 pound (lb)
1 kilogram (kg) = 35.273962 ounces (oz)
1 gram (g) = 0.035274 ounces (oz)

APPENDIX E

MEASUREMENTS

LENGTH

1 foot (ft) = 12 inches (in) = 0.3048 (m)
1 yard (yd) = 3 feet
1 yard = 36 inches = 0.9144 (m)
1 mile (mi) = 5280 feet (ft)
1 mile = 1760 yards (yd)
1 millimeter (mm) = 0.001 meter (m)
1 centimeter (cm) = 10 millimeters (mm)
1 centimeter (cm) = 0.01 meter (m)
1 decimeter (dm) = 0.1 meter (m)
1 decimeter (dm) = 10 centimeters (cm)
1 meter (m) = 100 centimeters (cm)
1 dekameter (dam) = 10 meters (m)
1 hectometer (hm) = 100 meters (m)
1 kilometer (km) = 1,000 meters (m)

LIQUID

1 cup (c) = 8 fluid ounces (oz)
1 pint (pt) = 2 cups
1 pint = 16 ounces (oz)
1 pint = 4 gills
1 quart (qt) = 2 pints
1 gallon (gal) = 4 quarts (qt)
1 imperial gallon = 1.2 US gallons (gal)
1 liter (L) = 1000 meters (m)
1 liter (L) = 1 cubic decimeter (dm^3)
1 milliliter (mL) = 0.001 liter (L)

WEIGHT

1 pound = 16 ounces (oz)
1 pound = 0.4536 kilogram (kg)
1 short ton = 2,000 pounds (lb)
1 long ton = 2,240 pounds (lb)
1 long ton = 1,016 kilograms (kg)
1 milligram (mg) = 0.001 gram (g)
1 centigram (cg) = 0.01 gram (g)
1 decigram (dg) = 0.1 gram (g)

1 gram (g) = 0.0352 ounce (oz)
1 kilogram (kg) = 1,000 grams (g)
1 kilogram = 2.2046 pounds (lb)
1 metric ton = 2,204.6 pounds (lb)
1 metric ton = 1,000 kilograms (kg)